Verbal Reasoning:
Cloze

The 11+ 10-Minute Tests

For the CEM (Durham University) test

Book 1

Ages
10-11

Practise • Prepare • Pass

Everything your child needs for 11+ success

How to use this book

This book is made up of 10-minute tests and puzzle pages.
There are answers in the pull-out section at the back of the book.

10-Minute Tests

- There are 31 tests in this book, each containing 25 questions.

- Each test is designed to target the cloze type of verbal reasoning questions that your child could come across in their 11+ test, and covers a variety of question types at the right difficulty levels.

- Your child should aim to score at least 21 out of 25 in each of the 10-minute tests.
  If they score less than this, use their results to work out the areas they need more practice on.

- If your child hasn't managed to finish the test in time, they need to work on increasing their speed, whereas if they have made a lot of mistakes, they need to work more carefully.

- Keep track of your child's scores using the progress chart on the inside back cover of the book.

Puzzle Pages

- There are 12 puzzle pages in this book, which are a great break from test-style questions. They encourage children to practise the skills that they will need in the test, but in a fun way.

Published by CGP

Editors:
Alex Fairer, Heather McClelland, Sean Walsh

With thanks to Claire Boulter and Maxine Petrie for the proofreading.

Please note that CGP is not associated with CEM or The University of Durham in any way.
This book does not include any official questions and it is not endorsed by CEM or The University of Durham.
CEM, Centre for Evaluation and Monitoring, Durham University and *The University of Durham*
are all trademarks of The University of Durham.

ISBN: 978 1 78294 599 4
Printed by Elanders Ltd, Newcastle upon Tyne
Clipart from Corel®

Based on the classic CGP style created by Richard Parsons.

Contents

You have **10 minutes** to do this test. Work as quickly and accurately as you can.

Fill in the missing letters to complete the words in the following passage.

1. Scafell Pike, [s][ ][t][u][ ][ ][ ][d] in the Lake District, is the highest

2. fell* in England. Standing at 978 metres, its [m][ ][ ][j][ ][ ][t][ ][c]

3. beauty and the [e][ ][ ][t][ ][n][s][ ][v][e] views from the summit make

4. it a [p][o][p][u][l][a][r] destination for experienced and novice

5. hillwalkers [ ][ ][ ][i][k][ ][ ]. Completing the challenging ascent is

   a considerable achievement, and there are understandably many people who

6. want to [c][ ][ ][ ][u][e][ ] this formidable fell.

7. While days on Scafell Pike are very enjoyable, it is [c][ ][ ][u][ ][i][ ][ ][l] to

8. take care at all times. It is important to be [p][ ][e][ ][ ][r][ ][d] and to

9. have the [n][ ][c][ ][ ][ ][s][ ][r][y] equipment, such as a map and a

10. compass. [S][u][ ][t][ ][b][ ][ ] footwear, such as walking boots, needs

    to be worn. The weather can be unpredictable, so warm and waterproof clothing

11. is essential. As long as a responsible [a][ ][p][ ][o][ ][c][ ] is taken, a walk

12. up Scafell Pike is [g][r][e][a][t][l][y] rewarding.

* fell — *hill*

Choose the correct words to complete the sentences below.

13.	Swimming is an accessible sport that is great at	☒ increasing ☐ expanding ☐ thriving ☐ growing fitness levels.
14.	It will be an	☐ accolade ☒ honour ☐ privilege ☐ acclaim to make a speech at the charity dinner next month.
15.	She showed	☒ great ☐ loads ☐ large ☐ high determination in finishing the race.
16.	As we left the cinema, we agreed that the film had been a	☐ satisfaction ☐ confusion ☐ fascination ☒ disappointment .
17.	Luckily, the traffic lights changed to green as their car	☐ emerged ☒ approached ☐ entered ☐ appeared .
18.	There has been a	☐ failure ☐ decline ☐ reluctance ☒ loss in the number of tourists visiting the aquarium.

19.	She ▪ expects ☐ thinks ☐ assumes ☐ believes to be home by 10.30 pm at the latest.
20.	Residents ☐ like ☐ have ☐ hope ▪ want something to be done about crime in the area.
21.	Plans for a new supermarket have ☐ distinguished ☐ detached ▪ divided ☐ distributed opinion in the town.
22.	I can see why the restaurant has ▪ received ☐ given ☐ awarded ☐ handed so many accolades.
23.	We need to protect this rare species ☐ until ☐ after ▪ before ☐ while it's too late.
24.	The weather ☐ raised ☐ exceeded ☐ increased ▪ improved over the course of our holiday.
25.	The new series of the police drama ▪ promises ☐ agrees ☐ will ☐ indicates to be the best one yet.

END OF TEST

/ 25

Test 2

You have **10 minutes** to do this test. Work as quickly and accurately as you can.

Select the most appropriate words from the table below to complete the passage. Write the letter corresponding to each word in the correct box.

A includes	**B** compete	**C** route	**D** consists	**E** their
F toughest	**G** impressive	**H** considered	**I** year	**J** its

The Tour de France is [1] to be an iconic road cycling race. It was created and

sponsored by the people behind the French magazine L'Auto in 1903 to gain publicity

for [2] paper and to increase sales. Made up of 6 stages and covering 2428 km,

60 riders assembled to [3] in the first ever Tour de France, with only 21 of them

managing to finish the race.

Today, the Tour de France has cemented [4] place as one of the most

prestigious events in the race calendar. It is held every [5] in July and [6]

of around 3500 km worth of road split up into 21 stages. The race takes place over 23

days, which [7] two rest days for the riders. The [8] changes every year,

winding its way through French towns and villages and over mountains.

The distinctive yellow jersey worn by the leader of the race was introduced in 1919.

The colour yellow was possibly chosen to match the pages of L'Auto. Winning this race

is an [9] achievement since it is regarded as one of the [10] physical tests

in the world.

Underline the correct words to complete the passage below.

Dear Kate,

I hope you are ^{11.} good | pleasing | well | favourable . We have arrived

safely at our cottage in Cornwall. The drive was long, but we tried to make as

^{12.} little | less | minor | few stops as possible. Our accommodation is lovely

— the sea is ^{13.} in sight | incite | insight | cited , and in the garden, most of the

flowers are in full bloom.

Yesterday, the weather forecast ^{14.} calls for | describe | insisted | predicted

sunshine for the week ahead, and we will endeavour to make the most of it by exerting

^{15.} oneself | it | ourselves | us on lots of long, scenic cliff-top walks.

After we had unpacked, we ^{16.} go ahead | proceeded | continue | set about

with our plan to visit our favourite pasty shop, but sadly it must have closed down

because it was no longer ^{17.} their | they're | there | theirs .

It's such ^{18.} [ashamed] [shameful] [shaming] [a shame] because they were the

^{19.} [most delectable] [delicious] [tastier] [more flavoursome] pasties I've ever had.

We are hoping to go to a farm tomorrow, ^{20.} [ware] [wear] [where] [were]

they make award-winning ice cream — hopefully they will still be open! The

^{21.} [loads] [quantities] [number] [size] of flavours on offer is incredible — there

are so many to ^{22.} [chose] [choose] [opt] [decide] from. On Tuesday night, we

are going to an outdoor theatre ^{23.} [opposite] [next] [adjacent] [aside] the park to

see a play. Between you and ^{24.} [I] [me] [myself] [them], I think it might be a bit

boring. However, I was ^{25.} [insured] [ensured] [assured] [unsure] that there would

be a picnic too, and I'm excited about that.

I look forward to seeing you when we get back.

From Lucy

END OF TEST

[/ 25]

Take a break and give these puzzles a go to practise your **word-making** and **spelling** skills.

Octopus Letter-Sort

Rearrange the letters on each octopus to find three words ending in the letter 'D'. Then, use the first letter of each word to find a secret three-letter word.

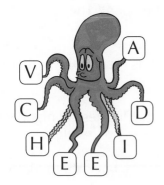

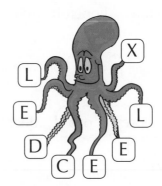

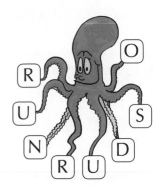

Word: _____

Word: _____

Word: _____

Three-letter word: ☐☐☐

Missing-Letter Riddle

Each of the words on the right has a missing letter. Identify the missing letters, then rearrange them to answer the riddle below.

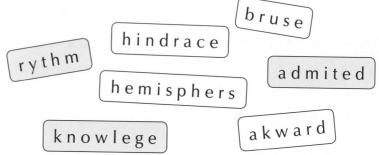

What whistles but has no mouth?   ☐☐☐ ☐☐☐☐

You have **10 minutes** to do this test. Work as quickly and accurately as you can.

Select the most appropriate words from the table below to complete the passage.
Write the letter corresponding to each word in the correct box.

A independent	B respects	C easy	D counterparts	E difference
F both	G lack	H develop	I expectancy	J prompting

It would be [1   ] to assume that white Bengal tigers are albino, or even an [2   ]

group of animals, but they are in fact the same as other Bengal tigers, just with a slight

genetic difference. Their fur is white because they [3   ] the pigment that makes

most tigers orange in colour. For this to happen, [4   ] of the parents of a white tiger

must have the unusual recessive gene for white fur; this occurs naturally only once in every

10 000 births.

The most obvious [5   ] between white and orange tigers is the colour of their fur

and their striking blue eyes, but in many [6   ], white Bengal tigers are the same as

their orange [7   ]. However, it has been suggested that white tigers have a shorter

life [8   ] than other tigers in captivity. This suggestion is based on the belief that as

humans started breeding white tigers for profit-based purposes, genetic defects began

to [9   ]. Some people argue that many of these tigers suffer from crossed eyes and

spinal issues, [10   ] lots of petitions to ban the breeding of white tigers.

Choose the correct three-letter word to complete the word in capital letters, so that it finishes the sentence in a sensible way.

Example: It can be **CHY** outside when it snows.

APP	ILL	EEK	ERR
☐	▬	☐	☐

11. The mixture should be **PED** into each of the cake cases.

OUR	EEL	AIR	ART
☐	☐	☐	☐

12. They watched the owl **SING** over the fields.

OAR	AND	EAR	CAR
☐	☐	☐	☐

13. I'm afraid I might have been too harsh when I **SPED** his invitation.

ARK	AWN	OUT	URN
☐	☐	☐	☐

14. It has been **ALED** that she knows the identity of the burglar.

LAY	ARM	LOW	LEG
☐	☐	☐	☐

15. He's very reliable and never **SHS** his responsibilities.

ARE	IRK	APE	EAR
☐	☐	☐	☐

16. You must make sure that you are **AING** by the rules at all times.

BAT	BID	BUS	TON
☐	☐	☐	☐

17. She was **REDED** for all her hard work.

FUN	WAR	MAN	DEN
☐	☐	☐	☐

18. Stefanie returned home extremely **REED** after two weeks away.

ACT	SUM	LAY	LAX
☐	☐	☐	☐

19. My friend bragged about **BING** me at darts for the rest of the evening.

ILL	EAT	EAR	END
☐	☐	☐	☐

20. The politicians will **DEE** the issues on television.

SIR	BAT	GAG	CAD
☐	☐	☐	☐

21. I **SNED** the crowd at the train station for my sister.

PAW	KIN	PAN	CAN
☐	☐	☐	☐

22. A look of terror **FLED** across her face.

AIL	OUR	ASH	OUT
☐	☐	☐	☐

23. Although he was wrong, he thought he was just **SING** the facts.

TAR	TAT	TOW	EAT
☐	☐	☐	☐

24. The sunbathers **BED** in the glorious weather all afternoon.

ASK	AIL	RAY	EGG
☐	☐	☐	☐

25. His car **STED** as he went up the steep hill.

RIP	ILL	ALL	ASH
☐	☐	☐	☐

END OF TEST

/ 25

You have **10 minutes** to do this test. Work as quickly and accurately as you can.

Fill in the missing letters to complete the words in the following sentences.

1. The Earth [r][ ][ ][o][l][ ][ ][s] around the Sun.

2. Her [d][ ][c][ ][s][ ][o][ ] to leave caused confusion among her friends.

3. He tried not to [d][ ][s][ ][ ][a][ ] his relief too openly.

4. The red deer is one of only two species of deer [ ][a][ ][ ][v][e] to Britain.

5. The [ ][ ][l][i][ ][a][t][ ] in India is very different to that at home.

6. We are [h][ ][ ][e][ ][u][ ] that he will get into university.

7. The discussion focused on the [ ][p][c][o][ ][i][ ][ ] election.

8. I'm not a fan of [ ][y][p][ ][c][a][ ] beach holidays.

9. I had a [ ][o][ ][d][e][r][ ][ ][l] time with my friends at the water park.

10. We hope to [g][ ][ ][i][ ][ ][ ][e] the shooting stars tonight.

12

Choose the correct words to complete the passage below.

I always looked forward to going to

11.
- ☐ stay
- ☐ remain
- ☐ break
- ☐ wait

with my grandad during

the summer holidays. We would spend

12.
- ☐ much
- ☐ every
- ☐ many
- ☐ large

hours pottering around in

his workshop, achieving very

13.
- ☐ few
- ☐ little
- ☐ minimal
- ☐ less

with our time. I would watch in

14.
- ☐ preoccupation
- ☐ fixation
- ☐ enthusiasm
- ☐ fascination

as he tinkered with his tools, and he would sometimes

carve little objects out of wood for me. He took great

15.
- ☐ dignity
- ☐ fulfilment
- ☐ respect
- ☐ pride

in his

workshop. He would categorise and store

16.
- ☐ all
- ☐ each
- ☐ everything
- ☐ entire

in carefully labelled boxes

and drawers, and I

17.
- ☐ impressed
- ☐ amazed
- ☐ marvelled
- ☐ astonished

at the pristine condition of each device.

He hung the larger tools, such

18.
- ☐ like
- ☐ as
- ☐ that
- ☐ a

saws, up on the walls, and I would eye

their menacing, gleaming teeth with

19. ☐ unease
☐ anxious
☐ apprehensive
☐ worried

20. ☐ However
☐ Although
☐ Regardless
☐ Despite

this, I felt

strongly compelled to touch the cool, hard metal, but I was always caught and received

a quick

21. ☐ rebuking
☐ scolding
☐ shouting
☐ criticising

. He was never really angry with me though. I think he

appreciated my

22. ☐ inquisitive
☐ curiosity
☐ attentive
☐ interested

about his hobby and valued my company.

He always smelled of sawdust and metal, even on those rare

23. ☐ purposes
☐ causes
☐ occasions
☐ reasons

when he

emerged from his workshop, and I am quite

24. ☐ certain
☐ assured
☐ clear
☐ obvious

that the same smell attached

25. ☐ herself
☐ themselves
☐ himself
☐ itself

to me when I returned home to my despairing parents.

END OF TEST

/ 25

14

It's puzzle time! These puzzles are a great way to brush up on your **vocabulary** skills.

Primate Puzzler

Fill in the sudoku puzzle with the letters D E F I A N T L Y.

Every row, column and 3x3 grid must contain the letters D E F I A N T L Y, but each letter can only appear once in each row, column or 3x3 grid.

		A				F		
E	L						D	T
	T		L	A	D		N	
D			I		L	Y		N
N	F	T		D		Y	L	I
L			F	T	N			E
	E		A	N	F		Y	
A	I						E	F
		Y				L		

Letter Ladders

Change one letter at a time to change the bottom word in each ladder into the top word. The two missing words must be real words.

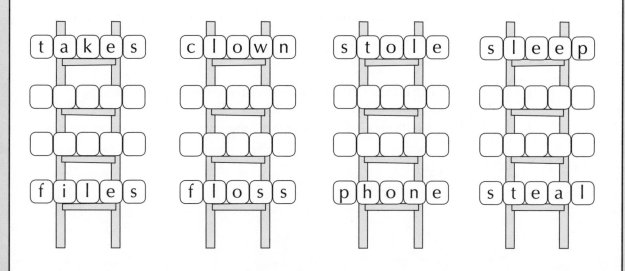

You have **10 minutes** to do this test. Work as quickly and accurately as you can.

Fill in the missing letters to complete the words in the following passage.

1.   On 5th November, many people in England [ ][ ]g[ ][ ]t up the sky

2.   with fireworks and h[ ]d[ ][ ]l around a bonfire. This celebration marks

3.   the 1605 Gunpowder Plot, which famously failed to [ ][ ]c[ ]e[ ]d.

        The plot was concocted by a group of plotters who secretly

4.   [ ]l[ ]c[ ]d gunpowder under the Houses of Parliament in an attempt

5.   to [ ]e[ ][ ]r[ ]o[ ] the building and kill King James I. They did this

6.   because they felt the government was treating them [ ][ ]f[ ]i[ ]l[ ]y

        — they were Catholics, and at that time, Catholics had to practise their

7.   [ ]a[ ][ ]h in secret.

8.   Before the plan could go [ ][ ][ ]a[ ]d, King James was made

9.   [ ]w[ ]r[ ] of the threat to his life, and soon after, Guy Fawkes was

10.   [ ]a[ ]u[ ][ ]t. He was arrested for high treason after being found

11.   [ ][ ]l[ ]w the Houses of Parliament. Fawkes was questioned

12.   [ ][ ][ ]u[ ]t the other plotters, and the King gave his permission for him to

13.   be [ ]o[ ]r[ ]u[ ]r[ ][ ].

Choose the correct three-letter word to complete the word in capital letters, so that it finishes the sentence in a sensible way.

Example: It can be **CHY** outside when it snows.

APP	ILL	EEK	ERR
☐	▬	☐	☐

14. All the wedding guests **GATED** on the dance floor at once.

HER	AID	ROT	THE
☐	☐	☐	☐

15. Martha was not used to **FING** in swimming competitions.

ARM	EAR	AIR	AIL
☐	☐	☐	☐

16. Jeremy was not good at **PING** between the lines.

ADD	AIR	ARK	ART
☐	☐	☐	☐

17. Brian liked to have a **WER** in the park on Sundays.

AND	AIL	ASH	INN
☐	☐	☐	☐

18. Over the summer, the field was filled with **FERS**.

EEL	LOW	ALL	RAM
☐	☐	☐	☐

19. Jessica bought a new **PAING** for her dining room.

END	RAT	TIN	SIT
☐	☐	☐	☐

20. The couple **CED** under the stars during a full moon.

ALL	AMP	OAT	HIM
☐	☐	☐	☐

21. My friend was **BLEEG** after she fell over in the playground.

RUN	AND	DEN	DIN
☐	☐	☐	☐

22. They had **ADED** really quickly to the new work routine.

APT	OPT	VIS	HER
☐	☐	☐	☐

23. Nadya bought a **STY** new jumper for Christmas.

CAT	AGE	RIP	ORE
☐	☐	☐	☐

24. Paul was **STING** to learn how to play the piano.

ALL	ART	AMP	AND
☐	☐	☐	☐

25. The teacher said that **EXDING** the summer holidays was not possible.

SEE	PEN	TEN	PAN
☐	☐	☐	☐

END OF TEST

/ 25

⏱ 10

You have **10 minutes** to do this test. Work as quickly and accurately as you can.

> Fill in the missing letters to complete the words in the following sentences.

1.   Bats are the only [m][ ][m][ ][a][ ][s] that can fly.

2.   Steve knew it was [ ][i][ ][f][i][ ][u][ ][t] to become an astronaut.

3.   The elderly man had [m][i][ ][p][ ][ ][c][ ][d] his glasses.

4.   Emma was helping to [c][o][ ][s][ ][ ][v][ ] the Honduran rainforest.

5.   Each tiger has stripes that are [ ][p][e][ ][i][ ][ ][c] to that individual.

6.   My village has just won a local tug of war [c][ ][n][ ][ ][s][t].

7.   Geena is able to speak [f][ ][u][ ][n][ ] French.

8.   The councillor strongly [ ][b][j][ ][c][ ][ ][d] to the proposed supermarket.

9.   The family decided to [a][ ][ ][n][d][ ][n] their original plan and eat out.

10. Kate thought the bookshelf would be [ ][t][ ][r][d][ ] enough to stay up.

Underline the correct words to complete the passage below.

If you're bored ^{11.} [at | with | in | off] holidays in hotels, you should consider

camping. The modern world is full of distractions, and camping offers a break from

^{12.} [they | them | those | their]. Camping is a good way to

^{13.} [loose | relaxed | calming | lose] yourself in nature and unwind.

One of the many ^{14.} [positive | upside | highlights | focusing] of camping

is the campfire. You can make some delicious meals by cooking on an open fire,

with smoky flavours ^{15.} [increasing | enhancing | reinforcing | building] a

variety of food. Communal cooking also allows people to come together — everyone

^{16.} [pitches in to | chips into | joins into | turns in to] get the food ready.

^{17.} [Without regard | Regarded | Respecting | With respect to] cooking

outdoors, make sure the grass is not ^{18.} [damage | charred | inflamed | alight] by

barbecues. Litter is also an important issue — plastic and glass containers can

19. | contribute | attribute | spread | advance | to environmental problems.

Experiencing nature and life 20. | along with | surrounded | apart from | among |

the trees is a key part of camping, so it is necessary to respect your surroundings.

Some people like to go on walks, and along secluded paths, they often don't meet

21. | anybody | pedestrian | nobody | other hiker | for many miles. Birds and

other animals can 22. | most | hardly | almost | ever | always be spotted, so it's

worth dedicating 23. | some thing | some time | someway | sometime | to the

world around you to see what you can find.

Walks are also a great way to burn off some energy, and they can tire you out to the

24. | extend | extension | extent | extensive | that when you return to camp, you'll

be ready for a good rest. There's more to camping 25. | then | though | that | than |

you may think — so why not give it a try?

END OF TEST

/ 25

Time for a break! These puzzles are a great way to sharpen up your **vocabulary** skills.

Animals Gone Wild

Some animals have escaped from the zoo.

Fill in the blank squares to identify
the creatures that have gone missing.

Then unscramble the blue letters in each group to identify four more animals.

c ☐ ☐ ☐ e ☐ ☐ ☐ n
☐ a ☐ n ☐ w ☐

→ Blue Letters: ☐

Animal 1: _ _ _ _ _ _ _   Animal 2: _ _ _ _ _

☐ i ☐ a ☐ ☐ ☐
a ☐ ☐ ☐ a ☐ ☐ r

→ Blue Letters: ☐

Animal 3: _ _ _ _ _ _ _   Animal 4: _ _ _ _ _

Anagram Arrangement

Unscramble the following words, then rearrange the words to reveal a fun fact.

v a e h
☐ ☐ ☐ ☐

c s o t h m a s
☐ ☐ ☐ ☐ ☐ ☐ ☐ ☐

w s c o
☐ ☐ ☐ ☐

u r f o
☐ ☐ ☐ ☐

_____ _____ _____

22

You have **10 minutes** to do this test. Work as quickly and accurately as you can.

Fill in the missing letters to complete the words in the following passage.

1.   Easter Island is a Chilean island l ☐ ☐ a t ☐ ☐ in the Pacific Ocean.

2.   The island is a ☐ t ☐ y named because it was first discovered by

3.   Europeans on Easter Sunday. The island is r ☐ n ☐ ☐ n e d for its

4.   statues, named moai. ☐ r ☐ u n ☐ 887 moai are believed to have been

5.   created. They are well-known for their e ☐ a ☐ g e ☐ ☐ t e d

    facial features, such as big noses and chins.

6.   ☐ n ☐ t i ☐ l ☐ y created by the native Rapa Nui people, the

7.   tallest of these statues ☐ t ☐ ☐ d s at nearly 10 metres high and weighs

8.   over 80 tonnes. It is not ☐ n ☐ w ☐ why these statues were created,

9.   but it is commonly ☐ s ☐ u m ☐ d that they were a sign of honour and

10. respect to leaders and late a n ☐ ☐ s ☐ ☐ r s.

11.   Many statues were carved from compressed ☐ o l ☐ a ☐ ☐ c ash

12. ☐ x ☐ ☐ v ☐ ☐ d from just one quarry, and hundreds of

13. moai r ☐ m a ☐ ☐ at the extraction site.

Choose the correct three-letter word to complete the word in capital letters, so that it finishes the sentence in a sensible way.

Example: It can be **CHY** outside when it snows.

APP ☐   ILL ▪   EEK ☐   ERR ☐

14. Three boats had been **WED** out to sea by the storm.

ANT ☐   ASH ☐   ARM ☐   ADD ☐

15. Night had **FEN** earlier than he had expected.

RAM ☐   LAM ☐   LOW ☐   ALL ☐

16. John is **PLING** a selection of roses in his window box.

ODD ☐   ANT ☐   ANN ☐   EAT ☐

17. Karim was writing a contemporary fantasy novel on his **COMER**.

BAT ☐   PUT ☐   BIN ☐   PAR ☐

18. Sarah was **GING** vegetables to sell at the market.

ROW ☐   ADD ☐   APP ☐   RAY ☐

19. Everyone had **COMTED** on the news that day.

FOR ☐   MIT ☐   BAT ☐   MEN ☐

20. The **FER** wanted more money for the milk he was selling.

ARM ☐   ALL ☐   LOW ☐   ILL ☐

21. The lid on the chest had been **NED** shut.

EAR ☐   ODD ☐   AIL ☐   ARE ☐

22. The man was sure he had **STED** someone familiar in town.

     COO   **POT**   **LOT**   **HUN**
     ☐   ☐   ☐   ☐

23. Irina wasn't sure if the water in the pan was **BING** or not.

     EAT   **AIL**   **ALL**   **OIL**
     ☐   ☐   ☐   ☐

24. During **DER**, the girl announced she wanted to be a boxer.

     ART   **AMP**   **INN**   **RAP**
     ☐   ☐   ☐   ☐

25. In autumn, the field was bathed in **GEN** light.

     OLD   **EVE**   **TRY**   **LAD**
     ☐   ☐   ☐   ☐

END OF TEST

/ 25

You have **10 minutes** to do this test. Work as quickly and accurately as you can.

Select the most appropriate words from the table below to complete the passage. Write the letter corresponding to each word in the correct box.

A point	**B** associated	**C** wary	**D** whether	**E** rather
F express	**G** appears	**H** creatures	**I** threaten	**J** estimated

Foxes are often [1   ] with the countryside, but so-called 'urban foxes' can be

found in towns and cities. It is [2   ] difficult to calculate the exact number of urban

foxes, but there are [3   ] to be around 33 000 of them in the UK.

Public opinion on urban foxes [4   ] to be divided. Many people class them as a

nuisance or a danger, but others [5   ] a strong liking for the feral [6   ]. Some

supporters of urban foxes [7   ] to the fact that these animals eat a lot of rats, which

helps to keep the rodent population under control.

It is a contentious issue as to [8   ] or not food should be left out for foxes. People

who are [9   ] of foxes might worry that feeding them will increase their numbers in

garden habitats and [10   ] other species. Some may also be concerned about foxes

entering their property in search of food.

Choose the correct words to complete the passage below.

We set sail three days

11.
☐ ago
☐ since
☐ ahead
☐ sooner

with the

12.
☐ eagerness
☐ hope
☐ desire
☐ want

of reaching the

coast that evening. Unfortunately, due to a spell of bad

13.
☐ weather
☐ humidity
☐ climate
☐ atmosphere

, we had to

14.
☐ stop
☐ shorten
☐ reduce
☐ shrink

our speed considerably. This caused

15.
☐ many
☐ some
☐ several
☐ plenty

of problems as our

food stocks rapidly

16.
☐ declined
☐ slipped
☐ descended
☐ collapsed

, which forced the entire crew to start rationing

17.
☐ anything
☐ whatever
☐ everything
☐ all

was left. While I believe I coped quite well with the hunger pangs,

the rest of the crew struggled. The captain

18.
☐ changed
☐ turned
☐ became
☐ emerged

incredibly annoyed at the

slightest fault or problem. Fights

19.
☐ exploded
☐ surfaced
☐ presented
☐ broke out

on deck between former friends.

The ship, which was at

20. ☐ start
☐ beginning
☐ first
☐ earlier

a symbol of hope and adventure, had become

an omen on the sea; a black spot of death hung over

21. ☐ all
☐ some
☐ every
☐ several

one of us. If we

did not

22. ☐ arrive
☐ return
☐ reach
☐ identify

to land soon, we would descend into madness. Last night, for

example, we thought we had spotted a ghost on the horizon. It took

23. ☐ several
☐ a lot
☐ one
☐ couple of

moments for us to realise that we were imagining things, and as the white light slowly

24. ☐ transferred
☐ changed
☐ replaced
☐ alternated

, we saw the outline of a lighthouse. Relieved, everyone looked over

to the land in

25. ☐ certainty
☐ positivity
☐ good spirits
☐ favour

.

END OF TEST

/ 25

You have **10 minutes** to do this test. Work as quickly and accurately as you can.

Select the most appropriate words from the table below to complete the passage.
Write the letter corresponding to each word in the correct box.

A available	B found	C houses	D roughly	E belonging
F complex	G resides	H occupied	I tourists	J spouse

The President of the United States of America [1 |] in the White House. Located

in Washington DC, the White House [2 |] includes the Executive Residence, the

West Wing and the East Wing, which can all be [3 |] in the main building.

The Executive Residence is [4 |] by the President and the President's family.

Many of the President's duties are carried out in the West Wing as it [5 |] not only

the President's office — the Oval Office — but also a large number of rooms for the

presidential staff. The East Wing contains office space for the President's [6 |] or

partner, who also has their own staff.

The White House sees a lot of people come through its doors, with [7 |] 100 000

people visiting each month. President Jefferson was the first to open the building to

[8 |] because he saw it as [9 |] to American people. Although they are not

[10 |] to the public, the White House has a swimming pool, a cinema, a tennis court

and a bowling lane, to name but a few of its facilities.

Choose the correct words to complete the sentences below.

11.	The family made it their goal to climb the ☐ highest ☐ high-rise ☐ many ☐ hilliness peak of the mountain.
12.	Sam is a ☐ dedicate ☐ devote ☐ passionate ☐ considerate fan of the new crime drama on television.
13.	Ivan ☐ knew ☐ found ☐ realized ☐ dreamt two porcupines while he was walking in the park.
14.	The journalist opened the box, ☐ accept ☐ save ☐ but ☐ bar it was empty.
15.	Emma loved to read all ☐ brands ☐ variety ☐ assortment ☐ types of books except for horror stories.
16.	Most people don't agree that barbecue sauce is far ☐ above ☐ admirable ☐ superior ☐ premium to mustard.
17.	Rebecca and her dog Bruno ☐ won ☐ conquered ☐ beat ☐ came first in the local talent show.

18.	The child was sent home	☐ away ☐ from ☐ against ☐ off	school because he was ill.

19.	Jacqueline's children	☐ loved ☐ beloved ☐ admired ☐ adored	to see the tigers at the zoo.

20.	The scientists worked for months on a way to	☐ cancel ☐ exclude ☐ eliminate ☐ reject	the virus.

21.	The man	☐ failed ☐ tried ☐ passed ☐ quit	to hail a taxi, but none of them would stop for him.

22.	Calista	☐ observed ☐ saw ☐ gazed ☐ watched	upon the lambs as they bounded across the field.

23.	John made the quiz extra-difficult to	☐ hardly ☐ well ☐ accurately ☐ really	test everyone.

24.	Kristina tried her very best to	☐ exceed ☐ transcend ☐ pass ☐ defeat	her medical examination.

25.	The waitress at the coffee house	☐ always ☐ ever ☐ anytime ☐ whenever	gave Ramiro extra biscuits.

END OF TEST

/ 25

Test 9

Breaktime! These puzzles will help you to practise your **vocabulary** skills.

Eye of the Storm

Use the clues below to fill in the whirlpool.

The last letter of each word forms the first letter of the next word.

When you have completed the spiral, unscramble the blue letters to find the bonus word.

1. Feeling sick or nauseous
2. A medium to large sailing boat
3. Large woody plants that have trunks
4. To fall below the surface of the water
5. Created when rope is looped and tightened
6. Pirates search for it
7. They protrude from the side of your head
8. Boating activity that takes place on water

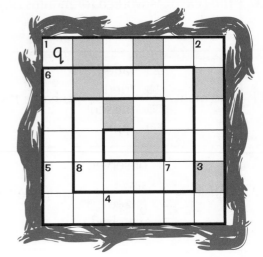

Bonus Word:

The whirlpool was a ⬡⬡⬡⬡⬡⬡⬡ phenomenon.

Word Chain

Write down four words that form a chain between "sail" and "tide". Change only one letter each time. The words you choose must match the definitions.

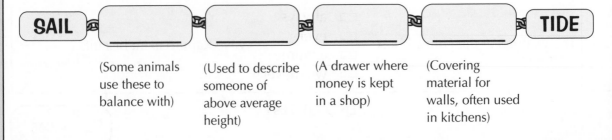

| **SAIL** | _____ | _____ | _____ | _____ | **TIDE** |
| | (Some animals use these to balance with) | (Used to describe someone of above average height) | (A drawer where money is kept in a shop) | (Covering material for walls, often used in kitchens) | |

You have **10 minutes** to do this test. Work as quickly and accurately as you can.

Fill in the missing letters to complete the words in the following sentences.

1. Venus is the only planet in our solar system that turns ☐ l o ☐ k ☐ i ☐ e.

2. The mayor d ☐ ☐ l ☐ ☐ e d that he was stepping down from office.

3. Being physically active is an important part of a h ☐ ☐ l ☐ h ☐ lifestyle.

4. My neighbour is ☐ x ☐ r e ☐ e l ☐ ☐ friendly, but very loud.

5. My friend was ☐ ☐ r a ☐ d I wouldn't show up for our trip.

6. The couple went for a r o ☐ ☐ n t ☐ ☐ candlelit dinner.

7. The fastest tigers are able to ☐ e a ☐ h speeds of up to 40 mph.

8. Akilah had ☐ a ☐ t e ☐ e ☐ the art of baking bread.

9. Camels have three eyelids to p ☐ o ☐ e ☐ ☐ their eyes from the sand.

10. I was pleased that my s c ☐ l ☐ t ☐ r e won first prize at the craft fair.

Choose the correct words to complete the passage below.

Louis Pasteur was not

11. ☐ sole
☐ unique
☐ single
☐ only

a chemist and microbiologist; he was also

an inventor and professor. He

12. ☐ grew
☐ gained
☐ constructed
☐ succeeded

two degrees, but it is his scientific

13. ☐ discoveries
☐ encounters
☐ concurrences
☐ introductions

for which he is most

14. ☐ perceived
☐ admitted
☐ approved
☐ recognised

. Pasteur believed that

microorganisms (e.g. bacteria) caused

15. ☐ brands
☐ products
☐ brews
☐ blends

such as wine or milk to turn sour,

so he developed a process which reduced the

16. ☐ score
☐ value
☐ number
☐ whole

of these microorganisms

without causing a huge change in

17. ☐ quality
☐ status
☐ capacity
☐ rank

. The pasteurisation process,

18. ☐ inscribed
☐ tagged
☐ named
☐ chosen

after its creator, involves heating liquid in order to kill microorganisms,

which helps to

19. ☐ repair
☐ cure
☐ process
☐ preserve

the liquid for longer.

Pasteur's developments in the field of microbiology led him to

20. ☐ catch
☐ emerge
☐ uncover
☐ originate

more about disease and vaccination. In 1885, he

21. ☐ consumed
☐ lost
☐ wasted
☐ used

a rabies vaccine

on a nine-year-old boy who had been

22. ☐ bitten
☐ pecked
☐ diseased
☐ polluted

by a rabid dog. The boy didn't

develop any symptoms, but he probably would have done

23. ☐ omitted
☐ lacking
☐ without
☐ deprived

the vaccine,

which implies that the vaccine had worked. Pasteur later opened 'The Pasteur Institute', a

charitable

24. ☐ building
☐ collection
☐ home
☐ organisation

that furthers research into the

25. ☐ interruption
☐ prevention
☐ obstruction
☐ interception

and

treatment of infectious disease.

END OF TEST

/ 25

You have **10 minutes** to do this test. Work as quickly and accurately as you can.

Fill in the missing letters to complete the words in the following passage.

1. A lack of gills or fins has not stopped [ ]u[ ][ ]a[n][ ] from exploring

2. the 71% of our [ ][ ]l[ ][ ][ ][t] that is covered by water. Instead, we strap

3. on diving gear and take the [ ][ ]l[ ]n[g][ ] below the surface. Differing

4. depths of dive require different [ ][ ]y[l][ ][s] of diving. Scuba diving is

5. very popular, and even the most [ ][o][ ][ ]c[e] diver can experience what

6. it has to offer. Scuba diving is a great [p][ ]s[ ][i][m][ ],

7. particularly for [ ][ ][ ]l[ ]r[i][n][g] coral reefs. However, less

8. experienced divers should only [ ]e[ ][ ][ ]n[d] to around 40 metres.

9. Due to the changes in [ ][ ]e[s][ ]u[ ]e and temperature as you

10. get deeper, more specialist equipment is [ ][ ]e[ ][ ][d] to reach greater

11. depths. Divers can use more [ ]d[ ]a[ ]c[ ]d diving suits, and they

    can use underwater transport, like scooters, to get to greater depths faster. As

12. this equipment is expensive, deep-sea diving [t][ ]n[ ][s] to be reserved for

13. more scientific or profit-making [ ][ ]r[p][ ][ ]e[s], such as

14. investigating marine life and [ ]e[ ]r[ ]h[ ]n[g] shipwrecks for

    treasure.

Choose the correct three-letter word to complete the word in capital letters, so that it finishes the sentence in a sensible way.

Example: It can be **CHY** outside when it snows.

APP	ILL	EEK	ERR
☐	■	☐	☐

15. The man **SLED** at me from across the street.

AMP	ADD	COW	TALL
☐	☐	☐	☐

16. Taliah **FLED** the kitchen surface before making her pizza.

AIL	APP	OUR	OUT
☐	☐	☐	☐

17. The wanderer headed towards the **GING** street lamp.

LID	LOW	OWN	EAR
☐	☐	☐	☐

18. The twins **PLED** in the sea for the first time.

EBB	AYE	EAR	ADD
☐	☐	☐	☐

19. Every morning, Paul **ATTS** to those who need his help.

END	ORE	AIL	INN
☐	☐	☐	☐

20. The blue team was **TED** with creating the tallest tower in ten minutes.

OUR	END	ASK	OIL
☐	☐	☐	☐

21. The journalists **SWED** around the actress as soon as they saw her.

APP	AMP	ARM	ILL
☐	☐	☐	☐

22. The King's army **DEFED** the invading troops, but it was a long and tiring battle.

    ERR   **END**   **ATE**   **RAY**

    ☐   ☐   ☐   ☐

23. Jenna thought the **FEST** thing was to share the cake.

    RAY   **ERR**   **EYE**   **AIR**

    ☐   ☐   ☐   ☐

24. After many months, the wartime spy finally **DEED** the message.

    BAT   **COD**   **COY**   **SIR**

    ☐   ☐   ☐   ☐

25. The **TLERS** both tried to go down the slide at the same time.

    RAW   **ODD**   **SET**   **RAT**

    ☐   ☐   ☐   ☐

END OF TEST

/ 25

You have **10 minutes** to do this test. Work as quickly and accurately as you can.

Fill in the missing letters to complete the words in the following passage.

1. After the death of Queen Victoria in 1901, Britain `e` `t` `e` `e` the

    Edwardian period — an era which took its name from the

2. `s` `c` `c` `e` `n` `g` monarch, Edward VII. During this period, over

    1.5 million people were able to make a living by gaining

3. `m` `p` `o` `m` `e` `t` in grand houses as domestic servants. Most

4. people in service `i` `b` `i` `e` `d` special servants' quarters in these

    houses, but despite living in close proximity to their masters, servants were

5. expected to make themselves `i` `i` `s` `b` `l`.

6. While there was a `t` `r` `i` `t` distinction between the family and the

7. servants, there was also a `h` `e` `a` `c` `y` among the servants

    themselves. In some houses, the butler and housekeeper were the highest

8. `r` `n` `i` servants, followed by people such as the cook and

    the valet; individuals like the scullery maid were at the bottom of this

9. `o` `c` `l` structure.

10. Edward VII `r` `g` `n` for only nine years before he died in 1910.

    He was replaced by his son, George V, who ruled throughout the First World War

11. and witnessed the dramatic `c` `n` `g` `s` that it brought about.

Underline the correct words to complete the passage below.

It was incredibly sunny last weekend, so my friend and I

12. (debated | organize | resolved | venture) to go to the park. James, to whom

I often 13. (wright | right | write | rite), was visiting from London, and we had

a fantastic time. First of all, we headed 14. (too | to | inn | in) the boating

lake. When we reached the shore, we went to a café and had an ice cream. I chose

chocolate sprinkles because I hardly 15. (never | at all | ever | regularly) have

them, and I wanted something different. Unfortunately, they had run out, so the

waitress substituted nuts 16. (with | about | for | in) the sprinkles instead. I was

17. (indicated | conscious | let known | conscience) that this wasn't what I had

ordered, but I enjoyed it anyway.

Once we had eaten our ice creams, we played crazy golf. I was the

18. (loser | looser | unsuccessful | defeat), although it wasn't a very even

game. James had agreed to 19. (lent | borrow | donate | lend) me his spare golf clubs, but unfortunately they weren't very good. I was also

20. [taken aback] [taken to] [took aback] [taken at] by James's skill — I had not

been 21. [alert] [aware] [familiar] [acquainted] of his talent. However, our

in-depth conversation 22. [over] [about] [concerned] [of] the merits of traditional

golf 23. [verses] [verse] [opposed] [versus] crazy golf should have warned me.

I played very badly, with neither skill 24. [nor] [but] [for] [and] concentration,

so James won by a long way. He wasn't very humble, and

25. [publicizes] [announce] [broadcast] [boasted] his success to anyone who

would listen.

END OF TEST

[/ 25]

Puzzles 5

You deserve a break! Have a go at these word puzzles and see how you do.

Simile Search

Complete the similes below
to create a list of words.

Then find the words in the word search.

1. as _____ as a cucumber

2. as _____ as a bat

3. as _____ as a flash

4. as _____ as a bee

5. as _____ as a feather

6. as _____ as a snail

```
S C E G F L K D J W B
C D O P Z C F N F J Z
N U Q O I N B I Y E E
S I B U L I X L B F F
N S Q U C E X B B A O
V N G E D S F O K E B
G J O G L S G K J Q U
U W A O O M Z N T A S
C E W J Z G Z H H A Y
P R N K M L I G H T I
A Y D Q J I Z Q H Z Y
```

Cube Words

Using just the letters in the cube, can you complete the sentences below?
You can only use each letter once in each word.

A	E	L
B	I	A
V	A	L

Every answer must use the letter 'i'.

The mud pie tasted ....

The field is .... to flooding.

A bath without a plug is just not ....

Michelle's party had a great ....

Can you find the nine letter word?   _ _ _ _ _ _ _ _ _

Hint: it's another word for 'free'

You have **10 minutes** to do this test. Work as quickly and accurately as you can.

Fill in the missing letters to complete the words in the following sentences.

1. The Smith family went on h ⬚ ⬚ ⬚ i ⬚ a ⬚ to visit their relatives.

2. Marianne has a lot of ⬚ e ⬚ c ⬚ l s because she loves stationery.

3. My best friend told me she'd had a strange ⬚ r ⬚ ⬚ m last night.

4. Andy visited the m ⬚ ⬚ ⬚ i ⬚ a l practice because he'd twisted his ankle.

5. Although the food was delicious, it was also quite g ⬚ e ⬚ s ⬚.

6. The b o ⬚ d ⬚ ⬚ s of France, Germany and Switzerland meet at one point.

7. I went to the greengrocer's, but they had run out of t ⬚ ⬚ a t ⬚ e ⬚.

8. Mathias wanted to be a doctor, but he struggled with s ⬚ i ⬚ ⬚ c ⬚.

9. The old lady hoped that ⬚ ⬚ t ⬚ r e generations would remember her.

10. Everything stored on the ⬚ a m ⬚ ⬚ a came out blurry.

Choose the correct words to complete the sentences below.

11.	Carrots are now known for their orange colour, but they were	☐ basically ☐ primarily ☐ originally ☐ generally	purple.
12.	Without a map,	☐ moving ☐ travelling ☐ navigating ☐ transporting	the streets of Venice is very difficult.
13.	Winter was Amal's	☐ favourite ☐ most ☐ popular ☐ good	season because the fire was almost always ablaze.
14.	You will need a	☐ admission ☐ ticket ☐ permission ☐ invite	to enter the building.
15.	Mark worked hard, but he	☐ floundered ☐ squabbled ☐ struggled ☐ contended	with geography.
16.	The old-fashioned sweetshop	☐ frequently ☐ extremely ☐ considerably ☐ hugely	ran out of jelly beans.
17.	The speaker felt	☐ dearly ☐ fully ☐ quite ☐ exactly	nervous about talking in front of so many people.

44

18.	The conjurer successfully managed to make the rabbit	☐ abandon ☐ escape ☐ disappear ☐ withdraw	.
19.	Jo loved visiting her grandma because she baked the	☐ foremost ☐ best ☐ leading ☐ prime	biscuits.
20.	It is important that we	☐ research ☐ study ☐ revise ☐ learn	from the mistakes we have made.
21.	My best friend is moving to a new school and will be very hard to	☐ recover ☐ restore ☐ replace ☐ reinstate	.
22.	Despite their strong smell, pickled-onion crisps	☐ taste ☐ flavour ☐ savour ☐ aroma	delicious.
23.	When I get angry, I try to	☐ depict ☐ assume ☐ perceive ☐ imagine	I am relaxing on a nice warm beach.
24.	This was the	☐ nearest ☐ closest ☐ strictest ☐ furthest	the team had got in the competition for years.
25.	Jack	☐ chose ☐ determined ☐ declared ☐ voted	for Jill to be the next class leader.

END OF TEST

/ 25

Test 13

You have **10 minutes** to do this test. Work as quickly and accurately as you can.

Select the most appropriate words from the table below to complete the passage.
Write the letter corresponding to each word in the correct box.

A associated	B retractable	C consumption	D events	E second
F precise	G oldest	H whittled	I interruption	J champion

The Wimbledon Tennis Championships is the [1   ] tennis tournament in the world.

It is one of four Grand Slam tournaments, but it is the only tournament to be played on

grass courts. The grass is cut to [2   ] specifications and is exactly 8 mm high. The

championships take place over fourteen days, with many [3   ], including the Ladies'

and Gentlemen's Singles, Doubles, and Mixed Doubles categories. Each of the single

draws starts with 128 players, who are [4   ] down to one [5   ] at the end of

each final. The finals take place on the [6   ] Saturday or Sunday.

There are many traditions associated with Wimbledon. One of the most popular

with spectators is the [7   ] of strawberries and cream, a dessert which has become

[8   ] with the competition. Not even the rain can dampen proceedings on Centre

Court because a [9   ] roof was installed in 2009. The roof can be opened or closed

in ten minutes, ensuring minimal [10   ] to play.

Choose the correct three-letter word to complete the word in capital letters, so that it finishes the sentence in a sensible way.

Example: It can be **CHY** outside when it snows.

APP	ILL	EEK	ERR
☐	▣	☐	☐

11. The football team **ADED** a new strategy to improve their defending.

HER	OPT	WAR	APP
☐	☐	☐	☐

12. A light was **FLING** in the distance and was very distracting.

AIL	ASH	APP	OUR
☐	☐	☐	☐

13. Mark had carved a **WON** elephant for his best friend's birthday.

ODE	OLE	ANT	TED
☐	☐	☐	☐

14. The young bear **WED** itself by basking in the sunlight.

ADD	ANT	AIL	ARM
☐	☐	☐	☐

15. Velma loved **PING** different foods together to create new flavours.

ADD	AIR	AIL	ANT
☐	☐	☐	☐

16. The traveller **WE** a letter to his relatives across the Atlantic.

HAT	HIT	HER	ROT
☐	☐	☐	☐

17. The dog was agitated and would not stop **BING** at the tall man.

OWL	ARK	AIL	URN
☐	☐	☐	☐

18. The girl was always losing her toy because she was **CLESS** with it.

LAW	OAT	ARE	HAP
☐	☐	☐	☐

19. Amy was tired and could not be **BORED** to do the washing-up.

ROW	THE	HER	ARE
☐	☐	☐	☐

20. The pair **SWED** stories about their lives when they were younger.

ASH	ILL	AMP	APP
☐	☐	☐	☐

21. The **DISCT** smell of freshly brewed coffee hung in the air.

PUN	TRI	TIN	ACT
☐	☐	☐	☐

22. The man **SED** at his watch and hoped the bus would arrive soon.

TAR	AND	LOW	EAT
☐	☐	☐	☐

23. The horse glanced nervously around the **POCK**, waiting for its owner.

AND	ADD	INN	ALT
☐	☐	☐	☐

24. Personally, I think fancy meals are **OVERED** because the portions are so tiny.

ACT	EAT	ADD	RAT
☐	☐	☐	☐

25. Even though he was getting older, the farmer still **TED** to his animals.

AMP	END	AIL	APP
☐	☐	☐	☐

END OF TEST

/ 25

You have **10 minutes** to do this test. Work as quickly and accurately as you can.

Fill in the missing letters to complete the words in the following passage.

The blue whale is thought to be the largest animal ever to have lived on our

1. planet, e c l i [ ] [ ] i [ ] g even the dinosaurs. A blue whale's tongue

2. can w [ ] i [ ] [ ] as much as an elephant, and a new-born calf can be heavier

3. than 30 men. They are also one of the l [ ] u [ ] [ ] [ ] t animals on Earth,

4. and it is thought that the [ ] o [ ] n d [ ] made by one blue whale can be

5. heard by another up to a d [ ] [ ] [ ] a [ ] c e of 1000 miles.

Despite their size, blue whales actually eat some of our planet's smaller

6. creatures, i [ ] [ ] l [ ] d [ ] n g plankton and krill. Instead of teeth, they

7. have brush-like plates that f i [ ] t [ ] r the water surrounding their food. A

8. whale takes in a [ ] o u [ ] h [ ] [ ] l of water containing krill, and as the

water moves back out, the krill get stuck in these plates and the whale

9. s [ ] a [ ] [ ] w s what is left.

10. Whales are mammals, so unlike some other m a [ ] [ ] n [ ] creatures,

11. they have l [ ] n [ ] [ ] instead of gills. This means they regularly have

12. to come up for air, which e [ ] [ ] [ ] e s them to human hunters. Due to

high levels of whale hunting in the early 1900s, the blue whale is now an

endangered species.

Choose the correct words to complete the sentences below.

13.	Since we live locally, we have	☐ available ☐ free ☐ exempt ☐ able	admission to the zoo all summer.
14.	Unfortunately, Gerry was told he needed an	☐ observation ☐ operation ☐ cast ☐ exercise	on his hip.
15.	I wanted to	☐ advice ☐ inform ☐ help ☐ guide	with the decorating, but I thought I would get in the way.
16.	Melinda's	☐ retaliation ☐ reception ☐ reaction ☐ answers	when she received her exam results made everyone smile.
17.	If Johnny eats any more cake, he'll need to buy some new	☐ clothes ☐ wardrobes ☐ attires ☐ apparels	.
18.	I am unlucky because I always seem to	☐ infect ☐ pass ☐ catch ☐ take	colds from other people.
19.	The attendant announced that the plane had been	☐ late ☐ slow ☐ behind ☐ delayed	indefinitely.

20.	While Kasia was on a school trip, her parents	☐ watched ☐ considered ☐ looked ☐ glanced after her dog.
21.	The comedian didn't know how he could keep the crowd	☐ amused ☐ laughed ☐ chuckled ☐ humorous for so long.
22.	The man who had been seen on the bridge was the main	☐ accused ☐ suspect ☐ crime ☐ villainous .
23.	It takes approximately four weeks for a caterpillar to	☐ transpose ☐ transfer ☐ translate ☐ transform into a butterfly.
24.	Unfortunately, the range in the bakery	☐ item ☐ aisle ☐ cakes ☐ ingredient was not very varied.
25.	The train from London was	☐ late ☐ behind ☐ after ☐ past pulling into the station at Preston.

END OF TEST

/ 25

The puzzles on this page will put your **vocabulary** and **word-making** skills to the test.

Say What You See

Use the clues below to create nine compound words.

Half of each word is written in the clue — the other half of the word is the way the clue is presented.

GUIDELINE

....

DRAGON

....

....

MAERTS

....

....

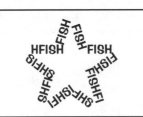

....

CUP
C
U
P

....

POST

....

....

HEART

....

You have **10 minutes** to do this test. Work as quickly and accurately as you can.

Select the most appropriate words from the table below to complete the passage.
Write the letter corresponding to each word in the correct box.

A mixture	B illuminated	C fully	D behind	E traditions
F vibe	G hive	H closest	I something	J natural

I absolutely love to visit the city of London. Although I like the countryside, I believe

there is [1] special about watching the landscape change from greenery to glass,

from [2] to man-made. There is a particular thrill to being part of a crowd that is

snaking its way through the underground before resurfacing in a completely new location;

it is the [3] thing to teleportation I can imagine.

I am constantly fascinated by the [4] of old and new and by how a city with so

many [5] can be so modern and ever-changing. Walking along the South Bank is

one of my favourite pastimes, as I get to [6] appreciate this contrast, observing the

Portland limestone of St. Paul's Cathedral [7] the swooping metal of the Millennium

Bridge.

By night, the city is transformed once again, as the buildings are [8] by a

spectrum of coloured light. It provides visitors with a second London, a London that is

still a [9] of activity but that has a completely different [10] .

Choose the correct words to complete the passage below.

When an animal comes under attack,

11. ☐ hunch
☐ premonition
☐ restraint
☐ instinct

kicks in.

'Self-preservation' is any behaviour that

12. ☐ aides
☐ favours
☐ primes
☐ seconds

survival. Animals are

13. ☐ equipped
☐ included
☐ appointed
☐ assembled

with many different self-preservation techniques. Fight and

14. ☐ worry
☐ scare
☐ horror
☐ flight

are the most common, protecting them not only from present dangers, but

from potential

15. ☐ warnings
☐ threats
☐ intimidation
☐ blackmail

too.

In the natural world, there are some intriguing defence

16. ☐ appliances
☐ gadgets
☐ utensils
☐ mechanisms

, for

example, an animal might

17. ☐ alter
☐ shift
☐ morph
☐ renovate

its shape to appear more

18. ☐ ambitious
☐ stately
☐ imposing
☐ grandiose

and threatening to others.

19.
- ☐ able
- ☐ manage
- ☐ capable
- ☐ succeed

Certain animals are _____ to change colour to better camouflage

themselves and avoid detection. Stranger examples include lizards that can shed

20.
- ☐ distract
- ☐ amuse
- ☐ engross
- ☐ fascinate

their own tails to _____ predators and escape their grasp. Once the tail is

21.
- ☐ endures
- ☐ maintains
- ☐ continues
- ☐ remains

detached, it _____ to move about, giving the lizard a chance to escape. The

22.
- ☐ skip
- ☐ discourage
- ☐ withdraw
- ☐ retire

opossum, a type of marsupial, will 'play dead' to _____ predators, but this

23.
- ☐ control
- ☐ authority
- ☐ regulator
- ☐ supervision

is an involuntary response over which it has no _____ . A slightly more

24.
- ☐ nastier
- ☐ gruesome
- ☐ repulsed
- ☐ corrupt

_____ approach is taken by the Texas Horned Lizard, which squirts blood from

25.
- ☐ aim
- ☐ point
- ☐ destination
- ☐ object

its eyes with the _____ of confusing potential predators.

END OF TEST

/ 25

Test 16

You have **10 minutes** to do this test. Work as quickly and accurately as you can.

Fill in the missing letters to complete the words in the following sentences.

1. Jessica had [m][ ][x][ ][ ] feelings about crossing the field full of cows.

2. The [a][ ][t][ ][o][ ][a][ ][t] spent nine months preparing for the mission.

3. He let me hold the medal, but it wasn't any [c][o][ ][s][ ][l][ ][t][ ][o][n].

4. Tyrese loved [b][ ][ ][ ][i][ ][g], especially now that he had a new oven.

5. The grapes in the bottom of my bag were [c][r][ ][ ][h][ ][d] by the potatoes.

6. If their tanks are large, [ ][ ][l][d][ ][i][ ][h] can grow to almost 50 cm.

7. It cost more than expected, but luckily he had money in [r][ ][s][ ][ ][v][ ].

8. Everyone [ ][h][ ][e][ ][e][ ] as the participants crossed the finish line.

9. The photograph of his wife was the man's most [p][ ][i][ ][e][ ] possession.

10. My friend asked if I wanted to go to the cinema this [ ][ ][e][n][ ][n][ ].

11. During our latest camping trip, we were all [ ][r][a][ ][m][ ][ ] into one tent.

Choose the correct three-letter word to complete the word in capital letters, so that it finishes the sentence in a sensible way.

Example: It can be **CHY** outside when it snows.

APP	ILL	EEK	ERR
☐	▬	☐	☐

12. The fruit must be **PED** before going in the crumble.

ADD	AIR	EEL	INN
☐	☐	☐	☐

13. The present I ordered online was expensive, but at least the **SPING** was free.

HOP	LIP	HIP	LAP
☐	☐	☐	☐

14. The soldier was **ADED** a medal for service to the country.

WAR	MEN	APT	OPT
☐	☐	☐	☐

15. The city arena **SED** an excellent production of 'Romeo and Juliet'.

LOW	WAY	AIL	TAG
☐	☐	☐	☐

16. Alexandra **RED** the biscuit tin for the very last custard cream.

OAR	BAR	AID	AIL
☐	☐	☐	☐

17. Charles Lutwidge Dodgson is more commonly **CED** Lewis Carroll.

ALL	OAT	RAT	ART
☐	☐	☐	☐

18. Noah found himself **TRED** in the hall of mirrors.

AIL	APP	ASH	EAT
☐	☐	☐	☐

19. My favourite stories are usually about knights and **LEGS**.

AND □   END □   AGE □   ACE □

20. The little boy burst into tears as he saw his balloon **FLING** away.

AIL □   ASH □   OUR □   OAT □

21. John and Jennifer's parties **CLED**, so I couldn't go to both.

ASH □   AIM □   EAR □   OAK □

22. Pablo loved nothing more than **SING** on a windy day.

AND □   END □   AIL □   NOW □

23. The little lamb **BLED** from across the field.

RID □   RAW □   END □   EAT □

24. Tony's father recently started his new job at the **SEE** plant.

SAM □   WAG □   END □   ARC □

25. The teacher **WED** the homework to be handed in by the end of the week.

ANT □   AIL □   INK □   ARM □

END OF TEST

/ 25

You have **10 minutes** to do this test. Work as quickly and accurately as you can.

Fill in the missing letters to complete the words in the following passage.

1. The River Nile is the longest river in the world with a ▢▢▢g▢h of

2. 6650 km overall. In its ▢▢▢▢ir▢ty, the Nile runs through ten

3. ▢o▢n▢▢ies, including Egypt and Uganda.

4. Seen from ▢b▢▢e, a green strip runs through the deserts of

    Egypt and Sudan, where the northern reaches of the Nile are located. This is

5. because the river ▢n▢r▢a▢es the fertility of the land, making

6. the area i▢▢al for farming. The Nile has become the centre of life,

7. ▢r▢v▢d▢ng water and a means for transporting food and

8. people, but it has also been ▢r▢ne to flooding.

    Since the construction of the Aswan High Dam in the 1960s, the majority of

9. flooding has ce▢s▢▢ downstream of the dam. Whereas flooding

10. can cause waterlogging, the dam allows for greater c▢▢▢▢r▢l

11. over water levels. The dam can also g▢▢e▢a▢e hydroelectricity,

12. which at times has po▢▢r▢d half of Egypt.

Underline the correct words to complete the passage below.

Millions of tourists will [13.] (throng | amassed | flock | congregate) in Blackpool

over the next few months as the Illuminations are switched on again. The six-mile-long

[14.] (attraction | entice | displays | features) includes over one million lights and

continues to [15.] (captivates | charming | enthral | delighted) people of all ages.

People described the Illuminations, when they were first unveiled,

[16.] (like | as | about | by) resembling 'artificial sunshine'. This is because they

were brighter than the gas lamps that [17.] (lined | positioned | bordering | fringes)

the streets back then.

Last year's display was [18.] (incorporated | consisted | composed | included)

of a variety of lights: coloured bulbs, lasers and neon signs were all used. The

Illuminations are built to [19.] (engage | prevail | contest | withstand) a wide

range of weather conditions, but they have to be repaired regularly, as they are

[20.] (partial | rusted | exposed | subjects) to the salty and corrosive sea air.

21. | Formally | Formerly | Previous | Already |, the features were removed to

be repaired and were taken to 22. | premise | complex | premises | lodge | owned

by the Illuminations Department. Nowadays, the work tends to be done on the spot.

Due to limited funds, one 23. | criticised | instructions | criterion | demanding | for

deciding how the maintenance should be carried out is the cost of the repair.

From September to November, visitors can see the lights from many different

24. | perspective | prospectives | prospecting | perspectives |. Lots of visitors drive

past them, while others walk along the promenade or take a ride on one of the many

illuminated trams, some of 25. | which | what | whose | whom | have been

modified to look like boats or trains. It is these special features that entice so many

people to visit the Illuminations.

END OF TEST

/ 25

Time for another puzzle. Let's see how good your **vocabulary** skills are.

The Adjective Crossword

Fill in the crossword by completing each of the sentences below with an **adjective**.

ACROSS

1   Grandma told us the ornament was very _____ so we had to be careful.

2   The woman looked _____ by my strange behaviour.

3   Michael _____ Gemma with his Halloween mask.

4   The car was very _____ — it had never broken down.

5   The elderly man had a book that was as _____ as he was.

DOWN

1   Aliona was very _____ when her cast was put on and didn't flinch once.

2   We went to a great circus last week — it was absolutely _____.

3   The fake painting looked almost as impressive as the _____.

4   The footballer was _____ enough to avoid the tackle.

5   Neville was _____ when he didn't come last in the running race.

You have **10 minutes** to do this test. Work as quickly and accurately as you can.

Select the most appropriate words from the table below to complete the passage.
Write the letter corresponding to each word in the correct box.

A consuming	**B** varieties	**C** ensuring	**D** cease	**E** transmission
F approaching	**G** inhale	**H** infected	**I** precautions	**J** symptom

When winter is ☐ 1 ☐, many of us may have to deal with a runny nose, a ☐ 2 ☐

of the common cold. Many colds are caused by viruses, and there are over two hundred

☐ 3 ☐. Due to this large number, we have a high chance of becoming ☐ 4 ☐ with

a cold more than once in a season, as our body can only fight off one cold at a time.

The most common method of ☐ 5 ☐ is coughing and sneezing, which infects the

air and other surfaces. When people ☐ 6 ☐ infected air droplets or touch infected

surfaces, they are at risk of catching the virus. Viruses can remain on these surfaces for

over 24 hours before they ☐ 7 ☐ to be active.

Even though there is no cure for a cold, there are various ☐ 8 ☐ we can take to keep

ourselves healthy. The most important of these is to frequently wash our hands, ☐ 9 ☐

they are as clean as possible. Even touching your eyes or nose with infected hands can

give the virus access to your body. Other measures include getting lots of sleep and

☐ 10 ☐ a balanced diet.

Choose the correct words to complete the passage below.

Even as a young girl, Florence Nightingale was certain her

11. ☐ existence
☐ purpose
☐ effect
☐ craft

was

to help people. But her desire to become a nurse was

12. ☐ dwindled
☐ terminated
☐ thwarted
☐ cancelled

by her family's

position in the social elite. Nursing was

13. ☐ trusted
☐ performed
☐ made
☐ believed

to be lower-class work, and this

created

14. ☐ battle
☐ combat
☐ conflict
☐ war

between Florence's high social standing and her medical ambition.

After years of disagreement, Florence's father eventually allowed her to

15. ☐ seek
☐ trace
☐ track
☐ pursue

nursing.

16. ☐ Since
☐ During
☐ When
☐ Meanwhile

the Crimean War, Florence travelled to Scutari in Turkey with 38

nurses. When greeted with utterly appalling conditions in the military hospital, Florence

made it her goal to

17. ☐ return
☐ redo
☐ reform
☐ reshuffle

hospital sanitation and

18. ☐ make
☐ cause
☐ prepare
☐ improve

patient

64

welfare. Her changes gave patients a much better chance of

19. ☐ remedy
☐ recovery
☐ cure
☐ help

, but led

Florence into the

20. ☐ mind's
☐ naked
☐ public
☐ urban

eye. This attention caused her to use a fake name in

order to live her life peacefully.

The

21. ☐ contact
☐ meeting
☐ collision
☐ impact

of her work is still

22. ☐ distinct
☐ locked
☐ fixed
☐ evident

today; she is heralded as

the founder of modern nursing. Florence led the way in nurse

23. ☐ training
☐ exercising
☐ working
☐ moving

, writing

many articles, as well as

24. ☐ describing
☐ opening
☐ visualising
☐ examining

the Nightingale school of nursing at St.

Thomas's Hospital in London, which

25. ☐ students
☐ fans
☐ teachers
☐ observers

can still attend today.

END OF TEST

/ 25

Test 20

You have **10 minutes** to do this test. Work as quickly and accurately as you can.

Fill in the missing letters to complete the words in the following sentences.

1. The [d] [ ] [l] [ ] [ ] [i] [ ] [s] were Michael's favourite animals at the zoo.

2. Her [s] [ ] [ ] [s] [ ] [o] [ ] [s] were blunt, so it took a while to unwrap the gift.

3. I [ ] [ ] [e] [v] [ ] [d] the remaining icing sugar on top of the cake.

4. The new [c] [ ] [ ] [p] [ ] [t] was more colourful than the last one.

5. The little girl wanted a [ ] [ ] [a] [n] [ ] [ ] [t] to keep herself warm.

6. The [b] [ ] [i] [ ] [ ] [e] that was recently destroyed was a useful crossing point.

7. All the children began collecting food for the [ ] [a] [ ] [v] [e] [ ] [t] celebration.

8. He got up before [ ] [u] [ ] [r] [ ] [s] [ ] , so it was dark outside.

9. The waitress was [c] [ ] [ ] [e] [ ] [ ] [l] not to let anything fall off the tray.

10. The burglar received a harsh [s] [ ] [ ] [t] [ ] [n] [ ] [e] in court.

11. The school had to [ ] [r] [a] [ ] [s] [ ] [o] [ ] [t] the pupils to the swimming gala.

66

Choose the correct words to complete the sentences below.

12.	The wildlife expert	☐ rescued ☐ preserved ☐ coaxed ☐ confined two little raccoons that were trapped in a hedge.
13.	Sandy couldn't control her	☐ careful ☐ irritable ☐ nervous ☐ hesitant laughter, even though it was embarrassing.
14.	Joan finally	☐ agreed ☐ authorized ☐ approved ☐ accepted my offer of a meal out at a fancy restaurant.
15.	The young boy had grown	☐ secured ☐ attached ☐ stuck ☐ affixed to his teddy bear.
16.	The	☐ aim ☐ desire ☐ focus ☐ strive of a good party is for everyone to enjoy themselves.
17.	Ben had been	☐ increased ☐ lifted ☐ promoted ☐ furthered to captain of the hockey team.
18.	The new animated film was really good, but it was far too	☐ short ☐ briefly ☐ less ☐ reduced .

Test 20

19.	The man ☐ motioned ☐ mimicked ☐ repeated ☐ remade	the instructions to ensure everyone knew their role.
20.	When my friend arrived, he ☐ rumbled ☐ banged ☐ crashed ☐ punched	on the front door until I answered it.
21.	The group found it very hard to find space on the ☐ crowded ☐ huddled ☐ squeezed ☐ massed	dance floor.
22.	Cathy loved to ☐ invest ☐ bargain ☐ gain ☐ purchase	new books when she received her pocket money.
23.	The schoolboy had a great deal of ☐ unity ☐ affinity ☐ sympathy ☐ connection	for the homeless man.
24.	Marielle was not a very good ☐ influence ☐ effect ☐ leader ☐ impact	on the other students.
25.	The man took ☐ more ☐ note ☐ pride ☐ down	of the recipe so that he could make it himself.

END OF TEST

/ 25

You have **10 minutes** to do this test. Work as quickly and accurately as you can.

Select the most appropriate words from the table below to complete the passage.
Write the letter corresponding to each word in the correct box.

A pedestal	B celebration	C represent	D gifted	E emblem
F designed	G holding	H famous	I copper	J alliance

The Statue of Liberty, also known as Lady Liberty, is one of America's most [1]

landmarks. French sculptor Frédéric-Auguste Bartholdi [2] the striking sculpture

with input from Gustave Eiffel (most famous for his own tower). Lady Liberty was

[3] to America by France as a [4] of one hundred years of American

Independence; the [5] between France and America was important in achieving

liberty.

Proudly standing on her [6] on Liberty Island, Lady Liberty has broken chains

at her feet and is [7] a slab with the date of American Independence engraved on

the front. Her glowing torch, which once welcomed immigrants to her shores, is now an

[8] of freedom around the world, and the seven spikes on her crown [9] the

seven continents and seas of the world. While the statue is now famous for its green-blue

hue, it was originally [10] in colour.

Choose the correct words to complete the passage below.

Although 25th December is the day on which many people

11. ☐ party
☐ perform
☐ celebrate
☐ deliver

Christmas, this is just one of the many Yuletide traditions that

12. ☐ vary
☐ divide
☐ contend
☐ amend

around the

world. Many Christmas

13. ☐ conventions
☐ etiquette
☐ formality
☐ behaviours

, such as decorating a tree, eating food with

family and giving gifts, are common across the

14. ☐ greater
☐ majority
☐ most
☐ many

of Christmas-celebrating

15. ☐ planets
☐ species
☐ cultures
☐ genders

.

Yet there are a lot of differences that help to add variety to celebrations. For example,

in

16. ☐ part
☐ any
☐ the
☐ some

countries, presents are opened on 24th December while in others this

17. ☐ passes
☐ lasts
☐ happens
☐ takes

a day later. Countries in the southern

18. ☐ culture
☐ hemisphere
☐ location
☐ world

celebrate

Christmas in the
19. ☐ opposite
   ☐ hot
   ☐ inside
   ☐ middle
of summer. But despite this variation, the idea of

children receiving gifts is
20. ☐ given
    ☐ evident
    ☐ exists
    ☐ available
in most cultures that celebrate Christmas.

Further
21. ☐ range
    ☐ alternative
    ☐ differences
    ☐ assortment
can be found in the treats left for Santa on Christmas

Eve. In Britain, it is customary to leave mince pies and milk,
22. ☐ still
    ☐ during
    ☐ however
    ☐ despite
, in

America, it is common to
23. ☐ concede
    ☐ provide
    ☐ allow
    ☐ sacrifice
cookies. In Italy, wine and the local culinary

24. ☐ speciality
    ☐ plate
    ☐ special
    ☐ tradition
is left for 'La Befana', a kind of witch who also delivers presents. Many

children also leave carrots for the reindeer so that they are not
25. ☐ served
    ☐ remembered
    ☐ forgotten
    ☐ excused
.

END OF TEST

/ 25

Puzzles 8

Exercise your **vocabulary** and **logic** skills with the puzzles on this page.

Word Square

Find the answers to the clues below using letters from the word square.
Each letter can only be used once in each word.

1. Another word for 'strength'.

_____

2. A tropical fruit.

_____

3. A way of saying 'to get off a train or bus'.

_____

4. Another word for 'hatred' (8 letters).

_____

5. A synonym of 'promise'.

_____

6. A fly that looks like a mosquito.

_____

Coded Message Conundrum

Here's a coded message. Each number represents a letter. Write the letter next to its number in the boxes below. Some of the code has already been solved.

`1` `2` `E`   `3` `E` `E` `1` `4` `5` `6`   `7` `8` `9` `C` `E`

`2` `9` `10`   `C` `2` `9` `5` `6` `E` `11`.   `3` `E` `E` `1`   `3` `E`

`9` `1`   `1` `2` `E`   `B` `R` `4` `11` `6` `E`.

1		3		5		7		9		11	
2		4		6		8		10			

You have **10 minutes** to do this test. Work as quickly and accurately as you can.

Fill in the missing letters to complete the words in the following passage.

1. The Harbin Ice Festival is an ☐☐n☐u☐☐l event that

2. ☐h☐w☐a☐s☐☐s some of the world's largest and most impressive
    ice and snow sculptures. The festival starts on 5th January and runs

3. until 5th February, although it is common for ☐x☐☐b☐t☐s to

4. open earlier and close later than this if the ☐o☐n☐i☐i☐o☐s
    are suitable.

5. Lots of the ice is s☐o☐☐c☐d from the Songhua River before

6. being constructed into ☐t☐i☐k☐n☐ sculptures that resemble

7. famous figures, m☐☐u☐e☐t☐s and buildings. These can be

8. found ☐l☐o☐g☐i☐e sculptures of animals and everyday
    objects. Usable ice sculptures are also very popular. People can try to

9. ☐a☐v☐g☐a☐e around a frozen maze, or glide down an ice slide.

10. Some sculptors even ☐n☐e☐g☐a☐e these slides into their
    design.

Underline the correct words to complete the passage below.

Hi Mandy,

We know you were 11. [wandering] [wondering] [considering] [viewing]

about our weekend. Well, on Saturday, we visited a wildlife park. It wasn't quite as we

had 12. [expected] [excepted] [accepted] [envisage], as the animals were in big

enclosures instead of small cages, and there were 13. [few] [less] [fewer] [lesser]

creatures than we had anticipated.

The 14. [most] [principality] [principal] [primarily] attraction was the tiger

enclosure, but the tigers were all just 15. [lied] [lie] [lay] [lying] down when we

saw them, so it wasn't very exciting. We also spotted lots of elephants.

16. [How] [As] [During] [If] we looked on, the elephants were squirting one

17. [spectators] [another] [more] [time] with water, which was funny.

We 18. [questioned] [queried] [asked] [pondered] the zookeeper why they were

doing that, and she said they were just having fun. In the shop, Mum

19. 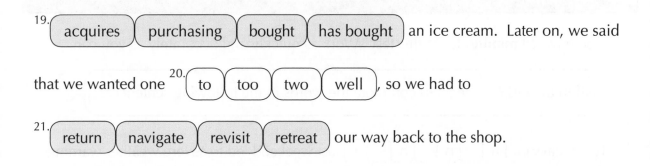 acquires | purchasing | bought | has bought an ice cream. Later on, we said

that we wanted one 20. to | too | two | well , so we had to

21. return | navigate | revisit | retreat our way back to the shop.

Unfortunately, we didn't spend as much time at the wildlife park as we

22. 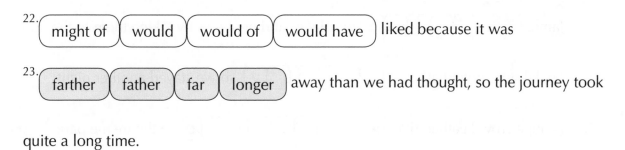 might of | would | would of | would have liked because it was

23. farther | father | far | longer away than we had thought, so the journey took

quite a long time.

Next week, our aunty, who 24. 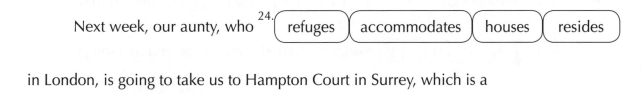 refuges | accommodates | houses | resides

in London, is going to take us to Hampton Court in Surrey, which is a

25. historic | history | historically | histories important building. We can't wait.

Love from Celia and Lynne

END OF TEST

/ 25

You have **10 minutes** to do this test. Work as quickly and accurately as you can.

Fill in the missing letters to complete the words in the following sentences.

1. Heavy ☐a☐n☐a☐l last weekend led to severe weather warnings.

2. The restaurant has a really ☐h☐rm☐☐g atmosphere in winter.

3. James ☐r☐at☐d his nieces and nephews by taking them to the zoo.

4. Luckily, the hotel had a ☐☐c☐n☐y, so we stayed another night.

5. A huge crowd gathered at the e☐☐r☐n☐e to the theme park.

6. John's father bought him a ☐el☐s☐o☐e for his birthday.

7. The f☐☐☐o☐y workers returned home at the end of a long day.

8. I stayed in the house all day, waiting for my ☐el☐v☐r☐ to arrive.

9. The ☐☐er☐g☐ lifespan of a housefly is 25 days.

10. Ollie broke his s☐☐☐☐d☐r and so couldn't go skateboarding.

11. The team took part in a ☐☐r☐at☐o☐ to raise money for charity.

12. My sister would not stop ☐o☐n☐n☐ about trivial problems.

Choose the correct words to complete the sentences below.

13.	The team ☐ made ☐ did ☐ executed ☐ carried	out the plan with military precision and accuracy.
14.	The boy had an incredibly realistic ☐ extract ☐ chime ☐ miniature ☐ hands	of Big Ben on his bedside table.
15.	Martin installed a ☐ compost ☐ foliage ☐ fountain ☐ puddle	in his garden to make it more interesting.
16.	Lynette's dog was more ☐ better ☐ obedient ☐ hungrier ☐ nice	when it thought it might get a treat.
17.	The best ☐ advert ☐ advise ☐ counsel ☐ view	I've received is to be yourself and not care what people think.
18.	Knowing what to buy people for Christmas is always a ☐ bane ☐ menace ☐ conundrum ☐ perplexity	.
19.	There was a sign ahead ☐ notifying ☐ detailing ☐ explaining ☐ displaying	us of an upcoming bend in the road.

20.	There was a	☐ disappointing ☐ pathetic ☐ terrifying ☐ pitiful thunderstorm last night, and we got some great photos.
21.	My friend said we should	☐ go ☐ look ☐ think ☐ consider visiting the museum during the holidays.
22.	The tour guide was less	☐ good ☐ helpful ☐ cultural ☐ interactive than we had hoped.
23.	Lizzie had to	☐ look ☐ stare ☐ observe ☐ sight the pugs as part of her most recent experiment.
24.	I	☐ cajoled ☐ beguiled ☐ urged ☐ duped Monica to eat the last slice of cake.
25.	The policeman deduced that it had been a case of mistaken	☐ personality ☐ witness ☐ identity ☐ criminal

END OF TEST

/ 25

You have **10 minutes** to do this test. Work as quickly and accurately as you can.

Select the most appropriate words from the table below to complete the passage.
Write the letter corresponding to each word in the correct box.

A occupants	**B** ensure	**C** partake	**D** venture	**E** tackle
F surrounded	**G** eccentric	**H** politely	**I** perched	**J** appreciate

Crestwood Castle, built in 1858 as a home for the wealthy and [1   ] industrialist

Sir Arthur Wray, is a remarkable place to visit. Occupying a lofty position [2   ] on

the top of a small hill by Lake Gardina and [3   ] by the imposing Hartscar mountain

range, this architecturally impressive structure will leave a deep impression on anyone

who comes here.

Everyone who visits Crestwood finds something to [4   ] about it. This castle

may not have been the scene of battles, but the colourful lives of its previous [5   ]

will [6   ] that you find its history fascinating. Why not [7   ] the castle's maze

and its many quirky features, such as hidden gates and misleading signs? You could

then [8   ] in a relaxing stroll around the extensive gardens or [9   ] further by

following the lakeside path.

There is no admission fee, but visitors are [10   ] encouraged to leave a small

donation, which will fund vital renovation work.

Choose the correct words to complete the passage below.

11. ☐ observe
    ☐ prescribe
    ☐ sanction
    ☐ determine

It is difficult to ___ an origin for pizza because it

12. ☐ changes
    ☐ turns
    ☐ depends
    ☐ follows

___ on what 'pizza' is defined as. For example, flatbreads have been popular

13. ☐ since   14. ☐ state
    ☐ as   ☐ notify
    ☐ with   ☐ tell
    ☐ for   ☐ give

___ ancient times, but it would be incorrect to ___ that the Ancient

15. ☐ present
    ☐ most
    ☐ least
    ☐ less

Romans ate pizza, or at ___ pizza as we know it today.

16. ☐ make
    ☐ opt
    ☐ pick
    ☐ choose

When making a modern pizza, most people ___ for a tomato sauce,

17. ☐ spiteful
    ☐ devious
    ☐ malicious
    ☐ poisonous

but originally, tomatoes were believed to be ___ . However, when the

peasants of Naples started covering their flatbreads with this red fruit, tomatoes soon became

a key pizza ingredient.

Although pizzas are

18. ☐ firstly
☐ lastly
☐ primarily
☐ widely

popular today, this tomato-based dish was

19. ☐ allowed
☐ deemed
☐ explained
☐ estimated

peasant food. When the aristocracy tried it, however, there was a

huge

20. ☐ grow
☐ expand
☐ rise
☐ ascend

in its popularity among a large

21. ☐ entity
☐ whole
☐ portion
☐ excerpt

of Italian society.

In 1889, Baker Raffaele Esposito was

22. ☐ appealed
☐ insisted
☐ invited
☐ demanded

to make a pizza for

Queen Margherita of Savoy. Esposito

23. ☐ added
☐ joined
☐ spruced
☐ garnished

one of his pizzas with the

colours of the Italian flag: red tomatoes, white cheese and green basil. Queen Margherita

24. ☐ enjoyed
☐ pleased
☐ delighted
☐ tantalised

it so much that the pizza now famously

25. ☐ tolerates
☐ steals
☐ bears
☐ reproduces

her name.

END OF TEST

/ 25

Time for a well-earned break. Here are some puzzles just for you.

Missing-Letter Riddle

Each of the sentences below contains a misspelt word. Find the letter that is missing from each misspelt word and write it in the blue box.

Once you have found all five missing letters, unscramble them to answer the riddle below.

1. Betty was an honest, hard-working and conscientius young woman.

2. Leo accidentaly spilt peas and gravy all over the kitchen worktop.

3. The dew on the garden made the grass glisen in the sunlight.

4. Gill had made a noticable improvement in her running time.

5. Bill has decided that he wants to be a playright when he grows up.

Riddle: What gets wetter the more it dries? [A]

Something in Common

For each group of words below, write down the word that can be added to the start or the end of all three words.

1. rain — fall — colour

....

2. birth — Sun — dream

....

3. cheese — pan — cup

....

4. fast — wind — heart

....

5. mark — work — worm

....

6. show — runner — works

....

82

⏱ 10

You have **10 minutes** to do this test. Work as quickly and accurately as you can.

Fill in the missing letters to complete the words in the following sentences.

1. I stood outside the ☐ t ☐ t ☐ ☐ n , waiting for my taxi to arrive.

2. The cheating at the chess championships was a ☐ c ☐ ☐ d ☐ l .

3. The peasants ☐ ☐ f i ☐ d the King's authority by staging an uprising.

4. The s e ☐ ☐ ☐ c e at the restaurant was excellent.

5. Small c l ☐ ☐ t ☐ ☐ s of people had gathered in the area.

6. He had a j ☐ a ☐ ☐ ☐ s nature, and he resented her success.

7. In Sweden, July is often the ☐ o ☐ t ☐ s t month of the year.

8. You can hire a bike for the ☐ u r ☐ t ☐ ☐ n of your holiday.

9. We went for a h ☐ a ☐ t ☐ pub lunch after our long morning hike.

10. The locals expressed their ☐ o ☐ c ☐ r n ☐ about the roadworks.

Underline the correct words to complete the passage below.

Crufts, one of the biggest dog events in the world, is held yearly, attracting thousands

of 11. | entrant | entrance | entrants | entranced | and spectators.

12. | Established | Found | Designs | Inspiration | by Charles Cruft in 1891, the

event has been 13. | modifying | developed | flourishing | increase | ever since.

However, since its 14. | initial | launch | origin | started |, Crufts has changed

significantly. Over the years, competitions focusing on different

15. | qualities | categorizing | division | breeds | have been introduced, for

example agility, in which dogs must complete an obstacle course as quickly as they

can. The competition is fierce, but in the 16. | midway | mist | midst | medium |

of the pressure, dog owners have to remain calm and

17. | collective | collected | collated | concerted |. Having gone through months

of preparation, they take hold of their dog's lead and walk confidently

18. | aboard | between | into | during | the ring, determined to win.

The Kennel Club, which regulates dog shows and keeps a register of pedigree dogs,

runs Crufts, and it has ^{19.} [published] [issues] [produce] [wrote] a Code of Best

Practice for Judges. This document describes how judges should remain

^{20.} [neutralized] [discriminated] [impartial] [unprejudice] and show every dog

^{21.} [engaged] [properly] [aptly] [equal] attention in the ring.

Crufts is regarded by many people as an event which

^{22.} [respect] [promoting] [celebrates] [tribute] dogs, but in recent years, attention

has been drawn to the welfare of pedigree dogs competing in the event. Efforts have

been made to ensure that dogs ^{23.} [seen] [seemingly] [deemed] [believe]

unhealthy are not chosen as winners. From 2009, judges at the show have been

^{24.} [authoritative] [approved] [license] [authorized] to remove dogs that they

believe are unhealthy from the ^{25.} [achievements] [judging] [actions] [umpires].

END OF TEST

[/ 25]

You have **10 minutes** to do this test. Work as quickly and accurately as you can.

Fill in the missing letters to complete the words in the following passage.

1.　　The ⬚r⬚u⬚⬚g⬚⬚ yet beautiful west coast of Scotland is sprinkled

2.　with islands that are rich in stunning ⬚⬚c⬚⬚⬚⬚r⬚y, fascinating

3.　history and wonderful ⬚⬚i⬚d⬚⬚⬚f⬚e. One of these is the

4.　Isle of Mull, which is a ⬚⬚o⬚v⬚⬚⬚y island in the Inner Hebrides.

5.　　Finding a place of peace and ⬚s⬚⬚c⬚⬚u⬚s⬚i⬚⬚ is not difficult

6.　on this island, and its richly ⬚v⬚⬚⬚i⬚d landscape offers a great deal to

7.　explore. The central part of the island is a mountainous ⬚⬚⬚g⬚i⬚⬚n

that is superb for walking. Rolling moorland is found elsewhere, along with

8.　forests, ⬚⬚a⬚m⬚⬚t⬚i⬚ coastlines and sandy beaches.

　　Mull is a great place to spot a sea eagle or to delve into the past by visiting

the island's castles and the stone circle. The town of Tobermory, the island's

9.　⬚⬚⬚p⬚i⬚⬚⬚l, is famous for its bright buildings on the

10.　⬚⬚⬚r⬚⬚o⬚⬚r front, which have become a popular tourist attraction.

Choose the correct words to complete the sentences below.

11.	The school production of 'Robin Hood' was ☐ diverged ☐ parted ☐ branched ☐ split into two acts.
12.	Emily ☐ scraped ☐ shaved ☐ scored ☐ scuffed the ice off her windscreen before going to work.
13.	The couple ☐ composed ☐ adorned ☐ painted ☐ portrayed the room different shades of blue.
14.	The day was unproductive and a complete ☐ use ☐ ruin ☐ waste ☐ squander of time.
15.	The detective found ☐ prediction ☐ clue ☐ witness ☐ evidence that could help solve the case.
16.	I didn't want to ☐ end ☐ desist ☐ exit ☐ cease trying, but I was not flexible enough to continue with yoga.
17.	Sinéad put a lot of ☐ achievement ☐ attempt ☐ attention ☐ effort into her homework.

18.	The smartphone is a relatively recent	☐ design ☐ invention ☐ production ☐ equipment	.

19.	The boy was totally	☐ fixed ☐ lost ☐ absorbed ☐ wrapped	in the book he received for Christmas.

20.	Joan had to	☐ reverse ☐ alter ☐ rearrange ☐ switch	seats with her brother so that she could see the screen.

21.	The rhinoceros beetle can	☐ shuttle ☐ lift ☐ channel ☐ conduct	objects up to 850 times its own weight.

22.	The most	☐ best ☐ chief ☐ important ☐ primary	thing they had to do was to keep themselves safe.

23.	We had to leave, but I didn't want to	☐ cut ☐ interrupt ☐ hold ☐ stop	him off mid-conversation.

24.	Raven had made a mistake, so she had to	☐ deal ☐ bare ☐ receive ☐ face	the consequences.

25.	The traveller	☐ removed ☐ unpacked ☐ emptied ☐ collected	his belongings out when he arrived on the island.

END OF TEST

/ 25

You have **10 minutes** to do this test. Work as quickly and accurately as you can.

Select the most appropriate words from the table below to complete the passage.
Write the letter corresponding to each word in the correct box.

A caused	B sight	C particular	D versions	E advantages
F community	G accessible	H recently	I limiting	J offer

Designers of electrical products always seem to be modernizing our devices. They have digitised our clocks, our TVs and our radios, and ⬚ 1 , they have come up with digital ⬚ 2 of books. Electronic books, or e-books, have ⬚ 3 a stir in the reading ⬚ 4 .

Many printed-book purists argue that e-books take away the sensory experience that books ⬚ 5 , that is, the feel and smell of a ⬚ 6 book or the ⬚ 7 of all your books on the bookshelf. It is also more difficult to share e-books with friends and family, ⬚ 8 the social aspect of reading.

However, e-books have become phenomenally popular. They are praised for their environmental ⬚ 9 because they don't use paper. They also allow readers to carry thousands of books with them at once; holidaymakers can take all their books with them, and the weight is the equivalent of just one paperback. Many older texts are also free in an e-book format, making these classic stories more ⬚ 10 to everyone.

Underline the correct words to complete the passage below.

When I fractured my ankle, it made me 11. [come | change | move | arrive] to

the realisation that it's annoying to be on crutches. One sunny afternoon, I

12. [snook | smuggled | sneaked | sneaks] into my neighbour's garden because it

had a great climbing tree in it. After climbing as high as I possibly could, I

13. [hang | hung | suspend | dangle] from a branch with both hands. I wasn't as

strong as I had thought, and I fell, landing on my left leg. I soon realised I had paid

14. [a debt | dearly | a high | at any] price for being overconfident — I was

15. [trapped | admitted | received | omitted] to hospital.

After 16. [scrutinising | appraising | looking | inspecting] at my leg, the

doctor moved 17. [next to | on to | off | onwards] examining my ankle, which he

announced was broken. He told me that I would need to be in plaster for six weeks.

Having the cast put on was less 18. [painful | paining | pain-free | painless] than I had expected — I had thought it would hurt a lot. After the cast had set, I tried out

the crutches I'd [19.] (attained | retained | maintained | obtained) from the nurse.

At first, I liked being on crutches, especially as my friends helped me carry my books

around school. However, it didn't take long for me to discover that they had

[20.] (selfish | thoughtlessly | addition | disregard) reasons for coming to my aid —

they wanted my crutches and loved [21.] (scheduling | timing | paying | making)

how long it took them to get from one place to another. However,

[22.] (her | their | they're | they) playing on my crutches began to get on my nerves,

as I was left [23.] (stranded | lonely | grounded | abandon) when they were using

them. I had to stand still as they [24.] (busying | bemuse | amused | occupy)

themselves. I couldn't wait to get back to [25.] (my | well | best | full) health.

END OF TEST

/ 25

A riddle a day keeps the doctor away. Test your **word-making** skills in the puzzles below.

Word Pyramids

Fill in the pyramid from top to bottom.
Add one new letter from the bottom
word each time. Use the clues to help.
The first two levels have been done for you.

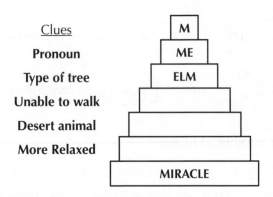

Clues
Pronoun
Type of tree
Unable to walk
Desert animal
More Relaxed

| M |
| ME |
| ELM |

MIRACLE

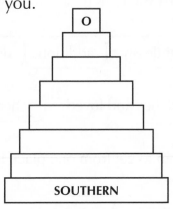

Clues
Not off
Unit of weight
Short letter/message
Word for rock
Antonym for corrupt
Decrease length

| O |

SOUTHERN

Letters on the Move

Remove one letter from each word in bold to solve the clues.

1. If you remove me from a **screw**, you will find me aboard a ship.
    (The letter ____ needs removing to make _____.)

2. If you remove me from a **pound**, you may find me near ducks.
    (The letter ____ needs removing to make _____.)

3. If you remove me from **medal**, you can eat me for dinner.
    (The letter ____ needs removing to make _____.)

4. If you remove me from **string**, what is left may hurt you.
    (The letter ____ needs removing to make _____.)

5. If you remove me from **claim**, you will find me under the sea.
    (The letter ____ needs removing to make _____.)

You have **10 minutes** to do this test. Work as quickly and accurately as you can.

Fill in the missing letters to complete the words in the following sentences.

1. My fancy-dress costume is going to [i] [ ] [ ] [r] [ ] [ ] [s] everyone.

2. The [ ] [f] [ ] [i] [ ] [i] [ ] [l] demolition of the Berlin Wall began in 1990.

3. I've been busy [r] [ ] [ ] [e] [ ] [t] [l] [ ], but I will definitely visit you soon.

4. Harry very kindly [ ] [r] [ ] [ ] [n] [g] [ ] [d] the whole surprise for me.

5. Red squirrels have been [ ] [b] [ ] [e] [r] [ ] [ ] [d] in the local park.

6. Our neighbour has been especially [h] [ ] [ ] [t] [ ] [l] [ ] towards us lately.

7. The [ ] [u] [a] [ ] [ ] [t] [ ] of the food at the restaurant is questionable.

8. This week's result was another [ ] [r] [ ] [u] [ ] [p] [ ] for the British athlete.

9. The [o] [ ] [i] [ ] [ ] [n] [ ] of World War One have been much debated.

10. It was [ ] [b] [ ] [i] [ ] [u] [ ] that Anna wasn't welcome at the party.

Test 28

Choose the correct three-letter word to complete the word in capital letters, so that it finishes the sentence in a sensible way.

Example: It can be **CHY** outside when it snows.

APP	ILL	EEK	ERR
☐	▣	☐	☐

11. Our triathlon club makes sure that it **CRS** for all abilities.

APE	ATE	ODE	OWE
☐	☐	☐	☐

12. She **SPED** out of the back door and was never seen again.

LIP	COO	HOP	NAP
☐	☐	☐	☐

13. Whoever was keeping track of the **SCS** didn't do a very good job.

OLD	OUR	ORE	OWL
☐	☐	☐	☐

14. There have been reports of loud, **TPING** music late at night.

RAM	HUM	RAP	ROO
☐	☐	☐	☐

15. As we neared the top of the hill, the car **SED** and then juddered to a halt.

EAT	TOW	LOW	OUR
☐	☐	☐	☐

16. Wendy **SCED** every room, but she couldn't find the letter anywhere.

OLD	HEM	OUR	OFF
☐	☐	☐	☐

17. The wildlife in this area **RES** on the efforts of our volunteers.

LIE	ACT	BUT	NEW
☐	☐	☐	☐

18. The Gunpowder Plot, led by Guy Fawkes, was eventually **FED**.

ILL	LAW	RAY	OIL
☐	☐	☐	☐

19. We found the play **ENING**, thought-provoking and also very funny.

JOY	GAG	ACT	COD
☐	☐	☐	☐

20. The distant noise of a gunshot made the birds **STER** in all directions.

POT	HAT	CAT	HUT
☐	☐	☐	☐

21. She stood outside the interview room, her stomach **CHING**.

AMP	URN	ARM	EAT
☐	☐	☐	☐

22. His horse, spooked by the sudden appearance of the lively dogs, **RED** up.

AID	EEL	OAR	EAR
☐	☐	☐	☐

23. The boy's grandma always gave him a **SWER** for Christmas.

ASH	EAT	TEA	ILL
☐	☐	☐	☐

24. The bad weather will **HER** the renovation works on the lighthouse.

OLD	EAT	OWL	AMP
☐	☐	☐	☐

25. Tariq's thoughts **STED** from his work to his weekend plans.

ALL	EEL	RAY	ART
☐	☐	☐	☐

END OF TEST

/ 25

You have **10 minutes** to do this test. Work as quickly and accurately as you can.

Select the most appropriate words from the table below to complete the passage. Write the letter corresponding to each word in the correct box.

A	tied	B	regarded	C	boundaries	D	atmospheric	E	while
F	figure	G	sought	H	subsequent	I	depictions	J	actually

Joseph Mallord William Turner, born in London in 1775, is [1] as one of

England's finest landscape painters. He pushed the [2] of landscape painting

and influenced the work of many [3] artists.

Turner is known for the skilful way he captured light to create dramatic and

[4] landscape paintings. He [5] to explore the power of the natural

world, depicting sunlight, fire and stormy seas in his paintings. Turner claimed to have

had himself [6] to the mast of a ship for four hours during a storm because he

believed experiencing stormy weather first-hand would help him understand exactly

what it was like. However, there is doubt as to whether this [7] happened.

Turner was a controversial [8] during his lifetime because his work challenged

the established style of landscape painting. It had an abstract quality, which was very

different to the realistic [9] of nature in traditional landscape paintings. Despite

this, he had many admirers [10] he was alive and still does today.

Underline the correct words to complete the passage below.

The town of Wolfton has become the outdoor gallery for the work of a mysterious

artist. Its [11.] (citizen | properties | inhabitants | council) have been left baffled

by sculptures that have appeared in various locations [12.] (around | via | up | at)

the town over the [13.] (past | passed | passive | pass) week. The sculptures are

white, life-sized human figures, which look as though they are from

[14.] (an earliest | a long | a bygone | a formerly) age. They include a chemist,

a farm labourer and a chimney sweep.

The [15.] (rational | motivation | intend | reasonable) behind the sculptures is

unknown, but some locals think that they highlight the town's history — a sculpture of

a tailor has been placed outside a shop that used to belong to a tailor, for example.

In all [16.] (likelihood | likeness | likely | probable), the sculptor is a local

[17.] (residence | residents | residential | resident), since he or she seems to know

a lot about the town. The [18.] (secreted | furtive | discreetly | unannounce) way in which the sculptures have appeared has ⁱ⁹·[put | aroused | saw | spark]

the locals' curiosity. Everyone in the town has an opinion on the identity of the sculptor.

However, there is already some ²⁰·[worries | concerns | misfortune | anxiety]

that the sculptures may be ²¹·[in | under | highly | at] risk. The mayor

²²·[raised | rose | brought | discuss] the subject of vandalism in a recent speech,

²³·[extracting | appeal | appealing | appalling] to residents to respect the statues.

'I can't imagine why anyone would disapprove of these sculptures,

²⁴·[yet | much less | much more | much alone] actively damage them,' he stated.

'I don't want the mystery sculptor to be deterred from installing more sculptures by a

²⁵·[cowered | cowherd | coward | cower] who thinks it's acceptable to graffiti all

over someone's artwork. Let's hope the sculptures continue to appear.'

END OF TEST

/ 25

Puzzles 11

It's definitely time for a break. Test your **spelling** and knowledge of **antonyms** below.

Back to Front

Solve the clues below to find four words that mean something different when they are spelled backwards.

a) Forwards I am some cooking utensils. Backwards I am a word for 'halt'.

— — — —

b) Forwards I am a quick glance. Backwards I am a word for 'retain'.

— — — —

c) Forwards I am a state of mind. Backwards I am a terrible fate.

— — — —

d) Forwards I store things. Backwards I am a prize.

— — — — — —

Mind Your Step

The frog needs to get from one lily pad to the other using the stepping stones — but he's only allowed to jump onto antonyms for the word 'innocent'. Draw lines to show the route he must take.

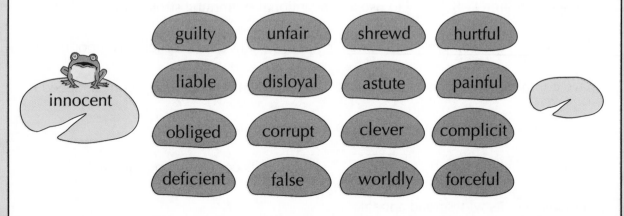

⏱ 10

You have **10 minutes** to do this test. Work as quickly and accurately as you can.

Select the most appropriate words from the table below to complete the passage. Write the letter corresponding to each word in the correct box.

A justified	B allowed	C possibly	D into	E bizarre
F blistering	G channel	H attire	I as	J attract

Imagine you're standing staring [1   ] a trench of cold, muddy, boggy water.

Your [2   ] consists of swimwear, a snorkel and a pair of flippers. You're about

to plunge into the murky depths. You would be [3   ] in wondering who would

[4   ] want to put themselves through such a thing. The answer can be found at the

annual Bog Snorkelling Championships.

Starting out [5   ] a charity event, the championships have grown in popularity

over the last thirty years and [6   ] people from all over the world. The challenge

is to complete two lengths of a 55-metre [7   ], which has been cut into a peatbog.

Competitors aren't [8   ] to use a conventional swimming stroke, and snorkels and

flippers are required. Wetsuits, however, are optional. One snorkeller is reported to

have completed the course in a [9   ] time of 1 minute and 22 seconds. Speed is

less of a concern for others, who take part wearing fancy dress.

Bog snorkelling may be a [10   ] sport, but its continuing popularity

demonstrates its widespread appeal.

As she leaned
11. ☐ within
☐ on top
☐ between
☐ against
the trunk of the tree with her eyes closed and her

legs swinging from the
12. ☐ vigorous
☐ forceful
☐ robust
☐ resolute
bough she was sitting on, Natalya
13. ☐ felt
☐ touched
☐ grasped
☐ caught

an unusually warm breeze. It was unexpected, but not so remarkable that she was

14. ☐ induced
☐ provoked
☐ roused
☐ prompted
from her doze. Moments later, however, a substance
15. ☐ akin
☐ like
☐ connected
☐ near

to sand excited her senses. This was an unusual
16. ☐ occasion
☐ occurrence
☐ period
☐ instance
as she was miles from

the sea. She opened her eyes in
17. ☐ revelation
☐ surprise
☐ suddenness
☐ hurry
, but quickly shut them again as her

eyes were pummelled by tiny grains. To her astonishment, she realised that it *was* sand, and

the
18. ☐ some
☐ less
☐ seldom
☐ few
grains that had prickled her skin were
19. ☐ rapidly
☐ belatedly
☐ punctually
☐ indefinitely
turning into

a swirling sandstorm. Her cheeks

20.
- [ ] resented
- [ ] wounded
- [ ] bared
- [ ] smarted

and sand caught between her teeth.

21.
- [ ] cower
- [ ] secure
- [ ] shield
- [ ] conserve

She desperately tried to ... herself by hurriedly pulling her jumper over

her head. As she clung to the tree, taking

22.
- [ ] compact
- [ ] shallow
- [ ] condensed
- [ ] minimal

, panic-stricken breaths,

she barely had time to take in what was happening before the air was

23.
- [ ] still
- [ ] stationary
- [ ] static
- [ ] immobile

again. It was over. She remained motionless for a

24.
- [ ] phase
- [ ] state
- [ ] duration
- [ ] moment

. In place of the green

rolling countryside, there was now a

25.
- [ ] nutritious
- [ ] plentiful
- [ ] vast
- [ ] copious

expanse of undulating sand dunes,

on which the sun beat heavily down.

END OF TEST

/ 25

You have **10 minutes** to do this test. Work as quickly and accurately as you can.

Fill in the missing letters to complete the words in the following sentences.

1. The lack of parking facilities at the doctors' surgery is an ⬚ u ⬚ r ⬚ g ⬚ .

2. John had all the d ⬚ s i ⬚ a ⬚ ⬚ e skills for his prospective job.

3. The monkey that escaped from the zoo ⬚ v ⬚ d ⬚ ⬚ capture for five days.

4. The company's ⬚ ⬚ s p ⬚ n s ⬚ to my email was very helpful.

5. Try adding spices to your meals for a more ⬚ n t ⬚ n ⬚ ⬚ flavour.

6. Listening to really loud music can ⬚ f ⬚ e ⬚ ⬚ your concentration.

7. The motivational speaker ⬚ n s ⬚ i ⬚ e d everyone in the room.

8. I had to ⬚ ⬚ d ⬚ r ⬚ heavy rain, strong winds and a leaky tent.

9. Specialist hedgehog food is available from certain ⬚ u ⬚ ⬚ l i e ⬚ s .

10. The Colosseum is one of the most n ⬚ t ⬚ ⬚ ⬚ e buildings in Italy.

11.	The industrial museum in Brenston is a	☐ capturing ☐ attracting ☐ addicting ☐ fascinating	place to visit.
12.	The exact meaning or purpose of Stonehenge remains	☐ missing ☐ unknown ☐ incognito ☐ misplaced	.
13.	The Vietnam War	☐ lastly ☐ lengthy ☐ usually ☐ finally	ended in 1975 when South Vietnam collapsed.
14.	Cheetahs are	☐ able ☐ competent ☐ capable ☐ efficient	of running at speeds of up to 65 miles per hour.
15.	There have been	☐ common ☐ numerous ☐ sizeable ☐ most	sightings of bears scavenging for food in bins.
16.	The newly	☐ refurbished ☐ modelled ☐ reformed ☐ conditioned	hotel is open once again for business this week.
17.	Lots of issues were	☐ lifted ☐ elevated ☐ increased ☐ raised	at the running club's committee meeting.

18.	I will have to go and	☐ pick ☐ collect ☐ gather ☐ assemble	the parcel up from the post office after work.
19.	My parents really enjoyed the concert,	☐ distinctly ☐ commonly ☐ especially ☐ basically	the encore.
20.	I think we really	☐ excelled ☐ exceeded ☐ transcended ☐ overshadowed	ourselves at the quiz this week.
21.	Large hooves help to	☐ endure ☐ sustain ☐ support ☐ maintain	a moose when it's walking in the snow.
22.	The school wants to raise	☐ shrewdness ☐ wariness ☐ alertness ☐ awareness	of the importance of healthy eating.
23.	For some, the Seaton Scramble is the	☐ remarkable ☐ intense ☐ ultimate ☐ extreme	hill-running challenge.
24.	The board game my niece received for her birthday is strangely	☐ expressive ☐ supportive ☐ addictive ☐ compulsive	.
25.	The construction of the Titanic took around three years to	☐ entire ☐ complete ☐ cease ☐ stop	.

END OF TEST

/ 25

Test 31

Give your brain a break with these puzzles. They test your **word-making** and **logic** skills.

Word Inspector

Write down as many four-letter words using letters from the word 'meaning' as you can in one minute. Then, write down as many four-letter words using letters from the word 'definition' as you can in two minutes.

m e a n i n g

d e f i n i t i o n

Treasure Trove Code

Use the hint to crack the code, then decipher the message to find out where the treasure is hidden.

In the code, 'HINT' becomes 'JKPV'

A B C D E F G H I J K L M N O P Q R S T U V W X Y Z

"VJG NQQV KU DWTKGF WPFGT VJG UJKRYTGEM"

Decoded Message: _____

_____.